Authors
František Sabol
Adrian Kolesár
Panagiotis Artemiou

SPECTRUM SLOVAKIA Series
Volume 12

Diseases
of the Aorta

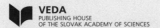

Bibliographic Information published by the Deutsche Nationalbibliothek
The Deutsche Nationalbibliothek lists this publication in the Deutsche Nationalbibliografie; detailed bibliographic data is available in the internet at http://dnb.d-nb.de.

Authors:	František Sabol
	Adrian Kolesár
	Panagiotis Artemiou

East Slovak Institute of Cardiovascular diseases, Ltd., Košice, 2015

Authors Acknowledgements:	Prof.Gabriel Valočík, MD, PhD.
	for animations and depictions,
	Ľubomír Špak, MD
	for dedication of pictorial sources of diagnostic
	methods (Computer Tomography, Nuclear
	Magnetic Resonance and Aortography),
	Dr.Prof. PhDr. Ján Sabol, DrSc.
	for language and editorial content correction,
	Assoc. Prof. Petr Němec, MD, PhD, MBA, FETCS
	and Assoc. Prof. Vilém Rohn, MD, PhD
	for their professional and kind reviews
	concerning this book, employees of Clinic
	of Cardiac Surgery Eastern Slovak Institute for
	Cardiovascular Diseases, Ltd. in Košice
	for their pleasing occupational milieu, in which
	authors may act, and moreover to our families
	for their support and patience.
Reviewers:	Assoc. Prof. Petr Němec, MD, PhD, MBA, FETCS
	Assoc. Prof. Vilém Rohn, MD, PhD
Cover design and Layout:	© Jana Sapáková, Layout JS.

ISSN 2195-1845
ISBN 978-3-631-66917-4   ISBN 978-80-224-1484-5
© Peter Lang GmbH   © VEDA, Publishing House
International Academic Publishers   of the Slovak Academy of Sciences
Frankfurt am Main 2016   Bratislava 2016

www.peterlang.com   www.veda.sav.sk

Table of Contents

Introduction, History of Aortic Diseases

It has been said: There is no disease more conductive to clinical humility than aneurysm of the aorta (Fig. 1, 2).

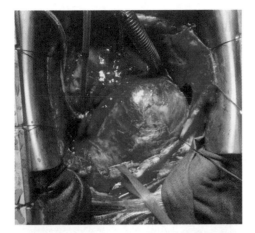

Fig. 1 _ Ascending Aorta Aneurysm (Sabol, 2012).

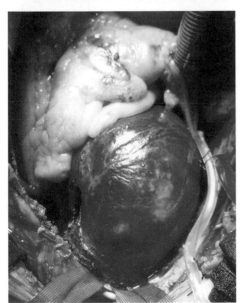

Fig. 2 _ Ascending Aorta Dissection (Sabol, 2013).

This Osler citation expresses the attitude of medicine towards aortic aneurysms during the second half of the 20th century. The development of the surgical treatment in 1952 accelerated a new interest about the diagnosis and treatment of aortic diseases. Acute aortic dissection in the past affected many intelligent individuals.

Among them were Albert Einstein, Lucille Ball, and many others. Some authors began to consider a possible genetic association between aortic aneurysm or dissection with the above average intelligence people (Elefteri-ades, 2007). The medical community began to realise the severity of the aortic destruction and its high morbidity and mortality. From the first years of the aortic surgery occurred sweeping changes in the surgical treatment, beginning from the excision of a part of the aortic wall and ending with the interposition of prefabricated vascular or biologic grafts necessary to maintain the aortic and the main branches continuity.

The first known description of dissection comes from Sennert, where in the 18th century the term dissection was first used by Maunoir. In the first half of the 20th century, the diagnosis of the aortic dissection was done exclusively postmortem. In 1923, Dshanelidze performed the first operation on a traumatic transection of the thoracic aorta, and twelve years later Gurin implemented an open fenestration due to malperfusion syndrome. In 1952, DeBakey and Cooley performed the first succesful radical resection of an aortic arch aneurysm (Cohn 2011). In 1954, DeBakey performed the first successful resection of a dissection of the descending aorta. In 1968, Bentall and De Bono performed the first replacement of an aortic valve and ascending aorta with a composite graft; their method with some modifications is used to this day.

Currently the classic aortic surgery with the use of cardiopulmonary bypass and deep hypothermia has very good results; however, it is highly invasive and requires a delayed recovery. Relatively new approaches to the treatment of the pathological aortic processes, like the implantation of an endovascular covered stent, the so called stentgraft are very promising, and patients do not need a long reconvalescence. Aortic segments that are difficult to access like the ascending aorta and the proximal part of the aortic arch currently are treated with a hybrid method, which is a combination of a surgical and an invasive treatment.

1.1 Anatomy of the aorta

The role of the aorta and its branches is to convey the blood to the whole body and to ensure the perfusion of all the organs. It (Fig. 3) commences at the upper part of the base of the left ventricle, and after ascending up to the level of the 2ⁿᵈ right sternocostal articulation as an ascending aorta (aorta ascendens) which is approximately 4-5 cm long.

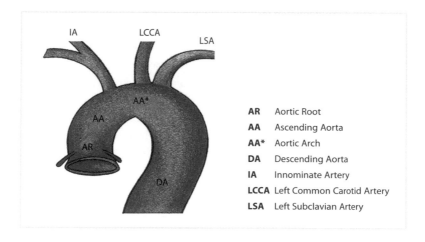

AR	Aortic Root
AA	Ascending Aorta
AA*	Aortic Arch
DA	Descending Aorta
IA	Innominate Artery
LCCA	Left Common Carotid Artery
LSA	Left Subclavian Artery

Figure 3 _ Topografic anatomy of the Aortic Root (Valocik 2013)

Next it continues as the approximately 6 cm long aortic arch that runs backwards from the right to the left side up to the level of the left side of the 3ʳᵈ thoracic vertebra. In this section begins the descending aorta that the diaphragm divides into the thoracic and abdominal aorta. Proximally, the thoracic aorta is situated on the left side of the thoracic vertebrae, and just above the diaphragm runs anterior to the thoracic vertebra so at the level of the hiatus aorticus is on the median plane. The abdominal aorta runs along the left side of the vertebrae and at the level of L4 where the aortic bifurcation divides into the two commune iliac arteries and runs in the midline along the sacrum to the tail bone (Borovansky 1979).

Aortic root

The aortic root (Fig. 4) begins above the aortic valve in a site called the aortoventricular junction. The aortic root in the literature is not quite right; it is called the aortic annulus. Anatomically, a real annulus has only the atrioventricular valves (mitral and tricuspid valve). The average diametre of the ascending aorta is 22 to 30mm (Cohn 2011). Just above the valve level is the aortic bulb which part of it are the three sinuses of the Valsalva, the left, the right, and the non-coronary sinuses. The first documented evidence of the Valsalva sinuses comes from the renaissance period from the descriptions and sketches of Leonardo da Vinci from the year 1531. In his notes, he describes the role of the aortic sinuses during the aortic valve closure. In 1740, Valsalva described the anatomy of the aortic sinuses for the first time. He considered that the main role of the aortic sinuses was the reduction of the stress exerted on the aortic valve leaflet during the systolic contraction, and another role of the aortic sinuses was associated with the coronary blood flow which happens during the diastolic phase.

From the left coronary sinus arises the left coronary artery, and from the right Valsalva sinus arises the right coronary artery. Proximally, the

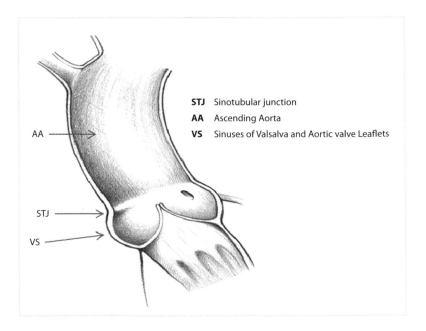

STJ   Sinotubular junction
AA   Ascending Aorta
VS   Sinuses of Valsalva and Aortic valve Leaflets

AA

STJ

VS

Fig 4 _ Depiction of Ascending Aorta and Root Components (Valocik 2013)

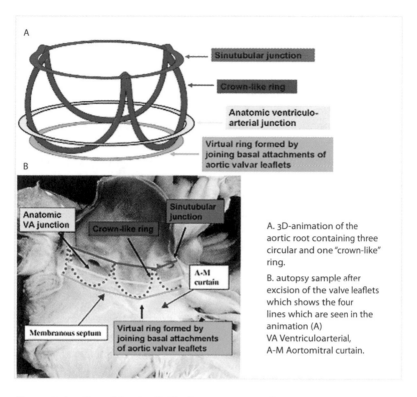

Fig. 5 _ Animation of the Aortic Root (Piazza et al. 2008)

aortic root is limited by the atrioventricular junction (AVJ), and distally is limited by the sinotubular junction (STJ) whose diametre is 20% larger than the AVJ diametre. The ratio between the muscular and fibrotic supportive tissue of the aortic root is between 25% to 85%, with an average of 47%. The middle of the subcommissural trigones makes up on average 54% of the overall diametre measured at the base of the venticles.

There is a significant difference between the supportive tissues of the right and the left aortic valve leaflets, but in the case of the non-coronary leaflet the supportive tissue is mainly fibrotic. In summary, we can say that approximately the 2/3 of the lower circumference of the aortic root is connected to the muscular part of the left ventricle and the other 1/3 is in continuation with the fibrous aortomitral curtain. At the aortic root are found three oval rings and one crown-like ring, which all prove its complex anatomy and physiology. Peaks (valve commissures), as is seen on Figure 5 (red ring, Fig. 5), together with the supportive tissue form a crown-shape ring.

The base of the crown (proximal) (green ring, Fig. 5) has a virtual oval shape ring formed by joining basal attachments of aortic valve leaflets. The peak of the crown (distal) that connects the valve commissures is an anatomic structure that is called the sinotubular junction (blue ring, Fig. 5). It is essentially the transition from the aortic root to the ascending aorta. On the opposite (proximal) side of the aortic root is the aortoventricular junction, thus the connection between the aortic root with the outflow tract of the left ventricle (yellow ring, Fig. 5). The aortic valve leaflet commissures are at the level of the sinotubular junction and basal attachments of the leaflets are at the level of the anatomic ventriculo- arterial junction. Below valve commissures and between the attachments two adjacent leaflets are found the subcommissural triangles. Their importance is to allow the expansion of the aortic root during the systolic phase of the left ventricle (Lansac et al., 2009).

Aortic valve and Coronary Arteries

A study which was conducted on 200 healthy individuals showed that the average width of the three aortic valve leaflets (free leaflet edge), thus of the right, left and non-coronary leaflet is 25.9mm, 25.5mm, and 25.0mm respectively.

The average height (from middle of the leaflet basal attachment to the free edge –nodulus Aranti) of the right, the non-coronary, and the left aortic valve leaflet is 14.1mm, 14.1mm, and 14.2mm, respectively. This considerable individual variability is proved by the fact that from the 200 specimens, only in five cases were the specimens identical among them.

In most people, the origin of the coronary arteries arises from the two sinuses of Valsalva, the right and the left. In a study with autopsy samples, the average distance measured from the origin of the artery to the basal attachment of the leaflet was calculated to be 12.6± 2.61 for the left coronary artery and 13.2±2.64 for the right coronary artery.

It is known that the angle between the left ventricular outflow tract (LVOT) and the ascending aorta changes with age. Adult individuals of age >60 years old have an angle between 90° and 120° while adolescent individuals of age <20 years old have an angle between 135° and 180°. Thus, LVOT passes to the ascending aorta almost in direct axis.

The aortic valve is closely related to the conducting system of the heart, the atrioventricular node (AVN). Part of the atrioventricular junction (AVJ) is at the apex of the Koch's triangle that is defined by the tendon of Todaro, the septal leaflet of the tricuspid valve and the culmination of the coronary sinus. The AV node is at close proximity below the apex of this triangle, in the membrane part of the interventricular septum, which is localised in the subcommisural triangle between the non-coronary and the right coronary aortic valve leaflets (Borovansky, 1979).

Ascending aorta

The ascending aorta has an average length of 5cm, and begins behind the left half of the sternum. It is covered by pericardium together with the pulmonary artery that runs parallel to the right side of the aorta.

The only branches of the ascending aorta are the right and the left coronary arteries, which supply the myocardium with blood. They are situated inside the right and the left coronary (Valsalva) sinuses just below the sinotubular junction (STJ) (Borovansky, 1979).

Aortic arch

The ascending aorta passes to the aortic arch at the level of the brachiocephalic ligament. From the aortic arch are (Fig. 4, 6) the three main aortic

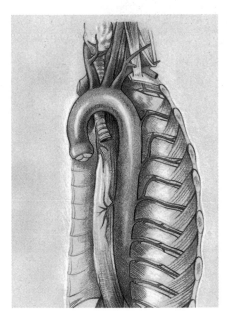

Fig. 6 _ Animation of the Aortic Arch and Descending Aorta (Valocik, 2013)

branches: the innominate artery, the left common carotid artery, and the left subclavian artery (see below).

The aortic arch begins at the level of the second intercostal space, initially running upwards and backwards directed to the left, in front of the trachea. Subsequently, it is directed backwards to the left. The level of Th4 (origin of the left subclavian artery) is directed to the left where it continues as the descending aorta. The upper margin of the aortic arch is approximately 2.5cm cranial from the manubrium of the sternum. From the front site the aortic arch is covered by the parietal pleura, the lungs, and by the remnants of the thymus gland.

Curving downwards, the left side of the aortic arch is in contact with the parietal pleura and the left lung upper lobe.

From the surgical point of view, there are three important nerves running very closely to the aortic arch:

1) left phrenic nerve
2) vagal nerve
3) recurrent laryngeal nerve (Fig. 7)

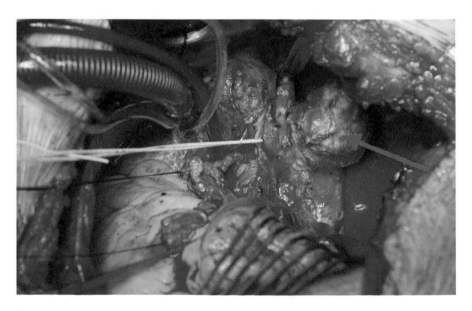

Fig. 7 _ Aortic arch with a postcoarctation pseudoaneurysm (blue arrow) and the adjacent nerves. The yellow rubber identifies the vagal nerve and the reccurent laryngeal nerve (Sabol et al., 2014)

The esophagus and the trachea are localised behind and on the right side of the aortic arch. From the aortic arch arise its branches (Fig. 3, 6). Below, is the bifurcation of the pulmonary artery, the left bronchus, and the ligamentum arteriosum that is the fibrotic changed arterial communication between (between the aortic arch and the pulmonary artery) the systemic and pulmonary circulation during the prenatal and early postnatal development. Just below the origin of the left subclavian artery, close to the ligamentum arteriosum is the so-called aortic isthmus (stenosis), which is the segment where the aortic coarctation occurs. Aortic coarctation is the pathologic process in which the aortic lumen is partially or totally obliterated.

From the aortic arch arise the three branches that supply blood to the head, the neck, and the upper limbs: the innominate artery (truncus brachiocephalicus), the left common carotid artery, and the left subclavian artery.

1. Innominate artery (truncus brachiocephalicus, TBC). It is the longest branch with a length of 4 to 5cm. It begins at the level of the 2nd intercostal space. It is directed obliquely upwards, backwards to the right at the level of the sternoclavicular articulation. It is divided into the right common carotid artery and the right subclavian artery. Behind, it is limited by the trachea. On the right side there are the right brachiocephalic vein, the vena cava superior, the right phrenic nerve, and the visceral pleura. On the left side there is the thymus gland, the origin of the left common carotid artery, caudal there is the thyroid gland veins, and the trachea. There are no branches from the TBC. Rarely from the TBC arise the inferior thyroid artery, which runs anteriorly to the trachea and supplies the lower lobe of the thyroid gland. Sometimes the thymic and bronchial branch arises from it.

2. Left common carotid artery. It is a paired artery, which begins from the upper part of the aortic arch that lies in the superior mediastinum and is directed to the left to the level of the backside of the TBC. It is divided into a thoracic and cervical part. The common carotid artery passes from the thoracic cavity to the cervical region through the upper thoracic apertura. The thoracic part has an upward direction, where at the level of the left sternocleidomastoid articulation continues to the cervical region as the cervical part. On the anterior side are the sternohyoideus and sternothyreoideuss muscles, the left brachiocephalic vein, and the thymus gland. On the posterior are the trachea, the esophagus, and the left recurrent laryngeal nerve. On the right it is the course

of the TBC, the venous system of the thyroid gland, and again the thymus gland. On the left side are the left vagal nerve, phrenic nerve, and the left bronchus including the left lung lobe. The cervical part of the artery, anterior below the sternocleidomastoid muscle, is obliquely directed upwards to the left where at the level of the upper margin of the upper lobe of the thyroid gland is divided into the external and internal carotid artery.

3. Left subclavian artery. It is a paired artery that supplies the left upper limb, partial regions of the cervical region, and the head. The proximal part of the artery arises from the aortic arch on the posterior of the left common carotid artery, at the level of Th4. It is in the upper mediastinum, and it is directed upwards into the cervical region and continues in an arcuate direction obliquely to the inner margin of the anterior scalenus muscle.

The second part begins from the margin of the anterior scalenus muscle and partially copies the course of the first rib, where it continues as the axillary artery. The left subclavian artery gives a range of branches, whose description exceeds the scope of this book.

Descending aorta

The descending aorta (Fig. 2, 6, 8) is localised in the posterior mediastinum. Visceral arteries (bronchial, esophageal, and pericardial) arise from it. From the surgical point of view the most important are the parietal branches. They are the intercostal branches which provide blood supply from the 3rd to the 11th intercostal space (blood supply to the first two intercostal spaces provides the left subclavian artery and its branches). The thoracic aorta is the thoracic part of the descending aorta. It begins at the level of Th4 and terminates at the level of Th12, the hiatus aorticus at the diaphragm and then continues as the abdominal aorta. At the beginning of its course, it is on the left side of the vertebra. Gradually it continues downward, turns to the midline, and at its terminal course it is localised in front of the vertebra. On the right side are the azygos vein, the right pulmonary artery, and the right pulmonary veins. On the left side there is the left bronchus.

The esophagus together with the nerve bundle are on the upper posterior mediastinum and on the right side of the aorta, on the lower posterior mediastinum are localised in front of the aorta close to the aortic hiatus on the diaphragm.

In the case of the aortic coarctation the continuity between the aortic arch and the descending aorta will be realised by collaterals between them. Potential collateral are:

a) the internal thoracic arteries through its pericardiophrenic branches and the superior epigastric artery branches which they create anastomoses with the inferior epigastric artery;

b) the inferior thyroid artery with the first intercostal artery;

c) the transversa colli artery creates large anastomoses with the posterior intercostal branches;

d) the large branches of the left subclavian and the internal thoracic artery create anastomoses with the side branches of the intercostal arteries.

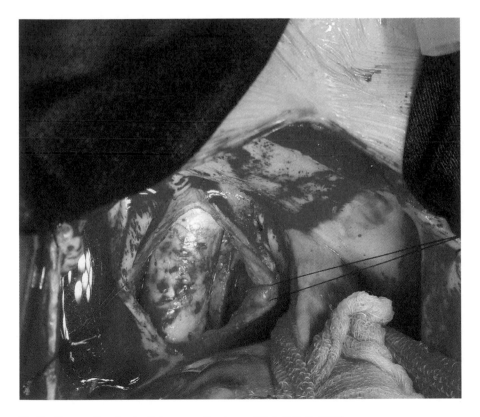

Fig. 8 _ Descending Aorta (intraoperative image)(Sabol et al., 2014)

In summary, we can state that through the collateral circulation there is blood supply to the abdominal and pelvic region. The collateral circulation for the lower limbs is realised by anastomoses between the internal thoracic artery and the epigastric artery.

The branches of the thoracic aorta are divided into the perivisceral, the pericardial, the bronchial, the esophageal, the mediastinal, the intercostal, the subcostal, and the upper diaphragmatic.

a) Pericardial branches. There are few small vessels that are localised on the back side of the pericardial sac.
b) Bronchial branches. These branches are different in terms of the number, the size, or the origin. There is only one right bronchial artery, which arise from the first intercostal or left bronchial artery. The left bronchial arteries are usually two and arise from the level of the thoracic aorta. The upper left bronchial artery arise from the level Th5, and the lower left bronchial artery arise from the level of the left bronchus.
c) Esophageal branches. There are four or five that arise from the anterior site of the aorta and they pass obliquely lateral to the esophagus, where they create a plexus of anastomoses with the branches of the lower thyroid artery and the ascending branches of the left gastric artery.
d) Intercostal branches. There are usually nine pairs. They arise from the posterior site of the aorta and they supply the nine intercostal spaces. The first and the second intercostal artery do anastomosis with the costocervical (arterial) trunk. The intercostal arteries of the lower section of the thoracic aorta supply the spinal cord through the segmental radicular arteries, which then supply the anterior spinal artery and the two dorsal spinal arteries. The most vulnerable section of the spinal cord is the one that is supplied by the large unpaired great anterior radiculomedullary artery (the artery of Adamkiewicz), which was described in 1882 by Adamkiewicz (Svensson et al., 1994). It has a variable origin and most often arise from the section between Th5 and L3 (Minatoya et al., 2002). After ligation of this important artery a very severe complication is caused – paraplegia or paraparesis due to spinal cord ischemia.

Abdominal aorta

The abdominal aorta crosses from the aortic hiatus of the diaphragm until the aortic bifurcation into the common iliac arteries at the level of L4. It holds a retroperitoneal position. At the level of the aortic hiatus, on the right side of the aorta is the beginning of the thoracic duct. On the right of the aorta passes the inferior vena cava.

From the abdominal aorta arise parietal (phrenic and lumbar arteries) and pair visceral arteries (the celiac artery, the superior mesenteric artery, the inferior mesenteric artery) (Fig. 9). Any ischemia of any of the pair visceral arteries is a severe complication and could have fatal consequences.

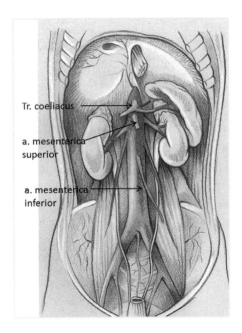

Fig. 9 _ Abdominal Aaorta (Valocik, 2013).

Tr. coeliacus

a. mesenterica superior

a. mesenterica inferior

1.2 Embryology and histology of the aorta

The aorta is the main artery, whose branches delivers oxygenated blood to the tissues. It begins from the so-called aorto-ventricular junction (AVJ) of the left ventricle. The division of the aortic segments are described in chapter 1.1.

Embryologic development of the aorta

One pair of intracardiac tubes are connected to one unit. Later this intracardial tube is elongated and contracted. It is divided into two venous sinuses, the atria, the ventricles, the truncus arteriosus, and the bulbus cordis.

During the fifth week of development, the division of the truncus arteriosus occurs.

Firstly, the folds of the truncus aorticus and the bulbus cordis are created. Later during development these loops are twisted 180°. Later, they are connected to form the aortic-pulmonary membrane, which is divided into the aorta and the pulmonary artery. During week four and week five of embryologic development, the bronchial arches are created, in which each arch has its own cranial nerve and artery. These arteries are known as the aortic arches, which begin from the upper terminal part of the truncus arteriosus and end on the posterior aorta. There are six aortic arches (Sadler, 2009; Fig. 10).

During development this arterial system changes and some arteries disappear. The fifth arch is usually hypoplastic and often is not created at all. During the period when the embryo is 4mm large, the first aortic arch disappears. Shortly, also the second arch disappears. The third arch is large. Fourth and sixth arches are in the process of development. When the embryo is 10mm large the first two arches disappear. Third, fourth and sixth are large. The truncal-aortic sac during this time is already divided, so the sixth arch is the continuation of the pulmonary artery.

During the later phase of the development, these changes happen:

- From the third arch, the common carotid artery and the first part of the internal carotid artery are created. The external carotid artery arises from the third arch.
- The fourth arch stays bilaterally. From its left side, the part of the aortic arch between the left common carotid artery and the left subclavian artery are created. From its right side the proximal part of the subclavian artery is created.
- The fifth arch is temporary and hypoplastic.
- The sixth aortic arch, known also as the pulmonary arch, provides an important branch that develops into the primitive lungs.

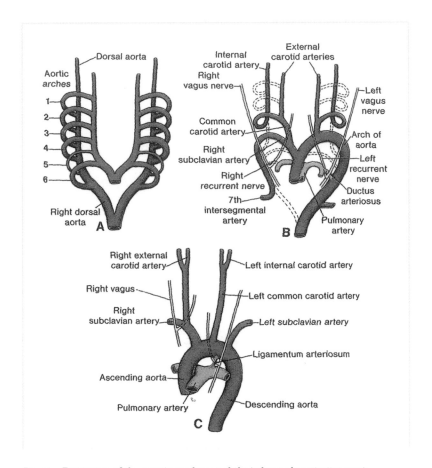

Fig. 10 _ Depiction of the aortic arches and their branches (Sadler, 2009).

Histology of the aortic wall and the arteries

Based on the histology structure we recognise in the arterial system three basic types of arteries:

1. elastic arteries, which are the main supply arteries, for example the aorta, the biggest body artery, the common carotid, and subclavian arteries, the pulmonary artery, and its branches;
2. muscular arteries which are the basic supply arteries, for example the radial artery;
3. arterioles, which terminate as capillaries.

The amount of the elastic tissue component of the arterial wall is decreasing as the diametre of the artery is also decreasing, and the amount of the smooth muscle component of the arterial wall is increasing. The arterial wall has three layers (Fig. 11).

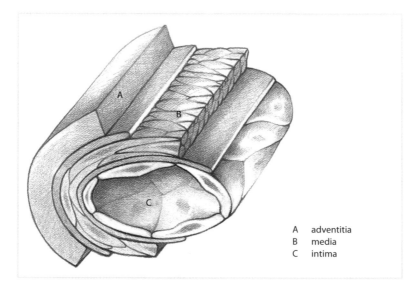

A   adventitia
B   media
C   intima

Fig. 11 _ Arterial wall layers (Valocik, 2013)

a) Internal layer that is composed from the endothelium (spinocellular) and the connective tissue. Below the connective tissue is the internal elastic lamina which divides the internal layer from the intermediate layer of the wall;

b) Intermediate layer contains elastin, collagen, smooth muscle cells, and the basic intercellular matrix. On the periphery, there is a layer of smooth muscle cells with a variable amount of connective tissue. Below this layer is a second layer of elastic fibers, the external elastic lamina, which divides the intermediate layer from the external layer;

c) External layer is composed from connective tissue, which is fused with the connective tissue around the artery.

The subendothelial connective tissue has diffuse fibroblasts and other cells that have the same microfunctions like the smooth muscle cells and are known as the internal muscle cells. As these cells age lipids are accumulated and the tunica intima gets thicker. This is one of the first signs of atherosclerosis. The elastic arteries have the internal layer thicker than the other arteries.

The thin layer of the connective tissue, below the endothelium allows the internal layer to move independently from the other layers during diastole when the systolic pressure is increasing. This is achieved by the concentric lamellae of elastic fibers that are found in the thick second layer of the arterial wall. In the human aorta there are approximately 50 such lamellae. The energy that is stored in the elastic fibers of the internal layer, allows the elastic arteries to function like "pressure reservoir" which drives blood during diastole. Smooth muscle cells and collagen fibers are found between the elastic fibers lamellae. Each elastic lamella creates with the interlamelar fibers and cells a lamellar unit. The external layer of the artery is thinner than the intermediate layer and contains collagen fibers and cells that usually are found in the connective tissue.

Larger arteries, like the aorta are accompanied by very small vessels which supply the external layer and the upper part of the intermediate layer of the wall.

Histology of the aortic root

The histology of the aortic root is characterised by the gradual relocation of the elastic fiber to the muscular ventricle. Proximally, the circular architecture (circular folliaceous architecture) is interrupted, there is an increasing amount of diffused collagen and the layers of the elastic tissue disappear. Subsequently, the collagen fibers are directly connected to the intermedial elastic tissue.

The aortic valve leaflets have different layers. The thickest one that is on the aortic site is fused with the annulus and forms the fibrosa layer. Another, reddish spongy layer is found proximally (towards the apex). This tissue is connected with the collagen tissue that is found on the annulus and together they create the subcommissural triangles. Each layer is covered with endothelium.

The aortic surface is covered with endothelium and the ventricular surface with endocardium.

The result of the semilunar attachments of the aortic valve leaflets is the creation of three triangular extensions of the left ventricular outflow tract up to the level of the sinotubular junction (STJ). These so called subcommissural triangles are not created by the ventricular myocardium but are

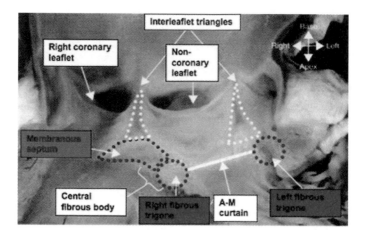

Fig. 12 _ Aortic root view from the left ventricle. Seen is the mutual continuity between the subcommissural triangles, the right and the left fibrous trigones, and the membranous septum A-M (aorto-mitral continuity) (Piazza et al., 2008).

created from the thin fibrous layer of the aortic wall that is found in the Valsalva sinuses. The apex of the triangle is localised in the site of the pericardial attachment, or in the case of the triangle between the left and the right coronary leaflet, the apex is localised on the tissue between the aorta and the anterior site of the sleeve – like the pulmonary infundibulum. Two of these triangles, which are bordered with the non-coronary leaflet, are in contact by fibrous tissue with the mitral valve and the membranous part of the interventricular septum (pars membrancea septi interventricularis) (Piazza, 2008, Fig. 12).

1.3 Pathophysiology and etiology of aortic diseases

The acute aortic dissection is the most lethal aortic disease. Aortic dissection exists in 5-10 out of 1000000 people per year (Fuster et al., 1994). In the USA, there are approximately 2000 occurrences of aortic dissection per year. Most affected are men between 50-70 years old, and incidence at an earlier age is associated with connective tissue diseases. The most common predisposing factor is arterial hypertension. According to the most extensive autopsy studies, only 15% of the acute dissections were diagnosed ante mortem. The prevalence of aortic aneurysms is, on average, 6 new aneurysms in 100000 people per year.

In principle, we distinguish three basic pathologies of aortic diseases. These are the aortic aneurysm (dilatation), the aortic dissection, or the aortic transection (Tab. 1). These pathologic states can affect whichever aortic part, locally or generalised. The domain of cardiac surgery are the diseases of the ascending aorta and the aortic arch. For the diseases of the descending aorta, the interdisciplinary approach between cardiac surgery and invasive angiology can be realised. The etiology of the development of the aortic aneurysm is multifactorial, most often a combination of different risk factors.

ANEURYSM	• aortic dilatation above physiologic values (approximately for the whole aorta $\geq 25mm/m^2$) • all the layers of the aortic wall
DISSECTION	• blood from the lumen penetrates intramurally, creates a layer separation of the aortic wall and a double lumen (real and false) • intramural blood flow through the entry site
TRANSECTION	• disruption of the aortic continuity úrazová etiológia (trauma etiology) • deceleration mechanism • next to origin of left subclavian artery

Tab. 1 _ Pathologic conditions of the Aorta (Cohn, 2011)

The risk for the development of aortic dissection and aortic aneurysm is increased in all the processes which are associated with diseases of the aortic wall, like connective tissue genetic disorders (Marfan syndrome, Ehlers-Danlos syndrome, and others), congenital heart defects (bicuspid aortic valve and aortic coarctation), and processes which increase the mechanical forces acting on the aortic wall (hypertension, atherosclerosis) (Tab. 2).

With the development of cardiac surgery and the extension of invasive diagnostic methods, inevitability has increased the number of iatrogenic dissections, pseudoaneurysms respectively (Tab. 2).

Gender has a role in the development of the disease, as men are twice more affected than women. The pathophysiologic basis of the aneurysms (or dissections) is the cystic medial degeneration of the media with frag-

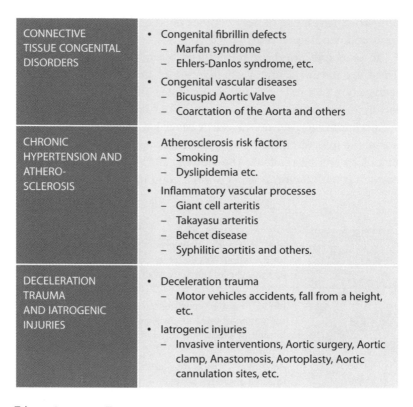

CONNECTIVE TISSUE CONGENITAL DISORDERS	• Congenital fibrillin defects
	  – Marfan syndrome
	  – Ehlers-Danlos syndrome, etc.
	• Congenital vascular diseases
	  – Bicuspid Aortic Valve
	  – Coarctation of the Aorta and others

CHRONIC HYPERTENSION AND ATHERO-SCLEROSIS	• Atherosclerosis risk factors
	  – Smoking
	  – Dyslipidemia etc.
	• Inflammatory vascular processes
	  – Giant cell arteritis
	  – Takayasu arteritis
	  – Behcet disease
	  – Syphilitic aortitis and others.

DECELERATION TRAUMA AND IATROGENIC INJURIES	• Deceleration trauma
	  – Motor vehicles accidents, fall from a height, etc.
	• Iatrogenic injuries
	  – Invasive interventions, Aortic surgery, Aortic clamp, Anastomosis, Aortoplasty, Aortic cannulation sites, etc.

Tab. 2 _ Aneurysm/Dissection risk factor (Cohn, 2011)

mentation of the elastic fibers and the loss of the smooth muscle fibers. As a result the wall loses its elastic properties and gradually dilates. During the systolic phase of the heart, the aorta expands and converts a proportion of the kinetic energy that is created during the contraction of the left ventricle, into potential energy for the aortic wall. During the diastole the aorta returns back, the aortic diametre is decreased, and the wall energy is converted back to kinetic energy for the forward flow. According to Laplace law, the aortic dilatation leads to an increase of wall stress on the basis of the intraaortic pressure. At the end, this results in aortic valve insufficiency and in an increased risk for aortic wall rupture or dissection. We recognise a real aneurysm whose wall is identical with the aortic wall stucture (intima, media, adventitia) and a pseudoaneurysm formed only by the adventitial layer of the aortic wall (Fig. 13).For the diametre of the aorta, there are normograms based on the age, the gender, and the body surface area of the patient. The average physiologic diametre of the aorta is 22 to 30mm, distally and gradually decreases. Simply about an aneurysm we talk if the diametre is more than 25mm/m² of the body surface area (BSA). The essence of the aortic dissection is the aortic wall (Fig. 14). Destruction of the aortic media leads to the development of an entry in the endothelium and to the intramural flow of blood (from the media until the subadventitial space). It leads to the development of a false lumen (dissection canal) in the aortic wall, which may spread in antegrade manner (distally, prograde, in the direction of the blood flow) or in retrograde manner (proximally, opposite the direction of the blood flow). According to the Laplace law, the risk for the development of dissection and rupture of the aorta is in proportion to the aortic diametre (extent of the dilatation). The most common site for entry is the part of the aorta above the STJ.

The etiology of the aortic transection is the second most common cause of death in motor vehicle accidents. Aortic transection is the cause of death in 75 to 90% of the cases. Approximately 8% of the patients survive more than 4 hours after the accident (Cohn, 2011). It is a specific disease, which is

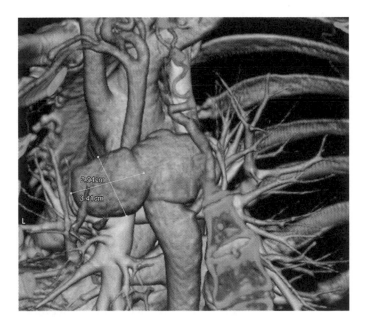

Fig. 13 _ Computer reconstruction of CT angiography showing an extensive pseudoaneurysm of the aortic arch and proximal part of the descending aorta (view from behind) (Sabol et al., 2014)

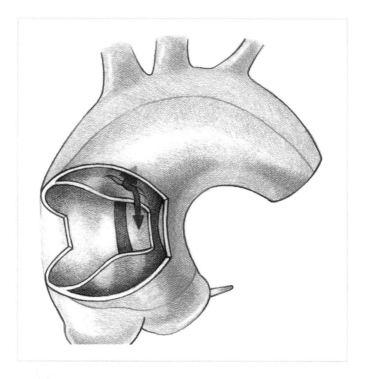

Fig. 14 _ Animation of the development of the aortic dissection
(red arrow – entry) (Valocik, 2013)

characterised by the complete disruption of all three aortic wall layers with
a several centrimetres dislocation of the intima and the media, while the
only layer that prevents the exsaqvination is the intact adventitia (entry is
in the whole aortic circumference).

It can happen throughout the whole segments of the aorta, from the
aortic root to the abdominal aorta; however, the most common site (35-55%
of the cases) is the aortic isthmus (the pass of the distal part of the aortic
arch to the descending aorta) (Fig. 15). The continuity of the aorta is main-
tained by the adventitia. Most common causes are motor vehicle accidents
and a fall from a heights. We talk about the so-called deceleration injuries.
The most common localisation of the transection at the aortic isthmus is
the result of the anatomic fixation of the aorta ands its segments. The descending aorta is fixed relatively tight to the spine and to the surrounding
structures; in the meantime the ascending aorta and the aortic arch are
minimally fixed. During deceleration there is a forward movement of the

heart, ascending aorta, and the aortic arch at fixed sites of the proximal part of the ascending aorta (below the origin of the left subclavia artery) with a knife effect.

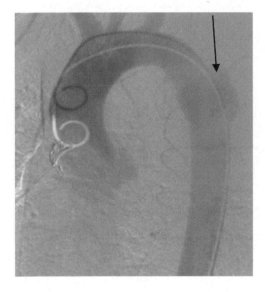

Fig. 15 _ Aortic Transection, arrow (Spak, 2011).

2.

Imaging Modalities

The diagnostic imaging modalities are very important for the diagnosis of the aortic diseases. In the case of emergency states, it should be quickly available with the minimal burden on the patient. Currently only two methods meet this criteria, the computer tomography (CT) and the echocardiography (TTE, TEE). Other methods like the magnetic resonance (MRI), the classic aortography (AG) with or without the use of the intravascular ultrasound (IVUS) are suitable for the diagnosis of the chronic states. For the diagnosis of acute states, they are second line methods. The sensitivity and the specifity of each method are seen on table 3.

Examination	Sensitivity	Specifity
"Classic" Aortography with contrast material	80–90%	88–95%
CT Angiography	90–100%	90–100%
Intravascular Ultrasound	94–100%	97–100%

Echocardiography
    Tranthoracic
    Transesophageal
	
	60–80%
	90–99%
		
		80–96%
		85–98%

Magnetic Resonance Imaging	98–100%	98–100%

Table 3 _ Sensitivity and Specifity of the imaging modalities

2.1 Echocardiography

The echocardiographic examination is one of the main diagnostic examinations of the aorta. It has an essential role during the diagnosis of acute and chronic aortic pathologic states perioperatively, in the operating room or in the outpatients department. It exists in two or three access modifications. The basic type is a non-invasive examination called the transthoracic echocardiography (TTE). Limitations include factors associated with the patient's type, emphysema or artificial lung ventilation. Another possibility is the transesophageal echocardiography (TEE). It is an ultrasound examination, where into the esophagus of the patient a transesophageal probe is inserted. It is an invasive diagnostic procedure, which has some risks; it can rupture the esophagus, cause hemodynamic instability, or increase burden to the respiratory functions of the patient.

We examine the patient either conscious (after preparation and fasting) or under anesthesia most often in the operating room or in the intensive care unit. The third modification is the epiaortic ultrasound that is performed in the perioperative period, when the epiaortic probe is put directly to the part of the aorta that we want to examine. However it is a relatively infrequent examination. TTE is a less exact diagnostic examination than the TEE.

The ultrasound helps in the differential diagnosis between potential pathologic states of the aorta, like the aneurysms (mainly the ascending aorta), the dissection (mainly ascending and descending aorta), and the intramural hematoma.

Diagnostic sensitivity during the examination of the distal part of the ascending aorta and the aortic arch in more than 40% of the patients can not be accurate mainly due to the presence of air in the tracheo-bronchial tree.

2.2 'Classic' Aortography with contrast material

Once was the gold standard in the diagnosis of the aortic pathologies, first used in 1939, it is today on the decline and it is used less frequently (Fig. 16). The disadvantage is the necessity of the amount of contrast material, extensive exposure to the radiation, local complications at the puncture site, and finally the worst sensitivity in the diagnosis of the aortic dissection compared with the computer tomography, the magnetic resonance or the transesophageal echocardiography.

The aortography provides an image of the aortic lumen and can be an asset in the differential diagnosis of different diseases that have characteristic findings: for example, this can be the dilation of the aortic annulus (aorto-ventricular junction), with the characteristic picture of a pear. It is caused by the more extensive dilatation of the heart ventricles in comparison with the dilatation of the ascending aorta. Next can be the classic saccular pseudoaneurysm that the aortographic examination exactly value. In indicated cases it offers an option in which at the same time are examined the coronary arteries and partially is examined the state of the left heart ventricle (coronarography and ventriculography examination).

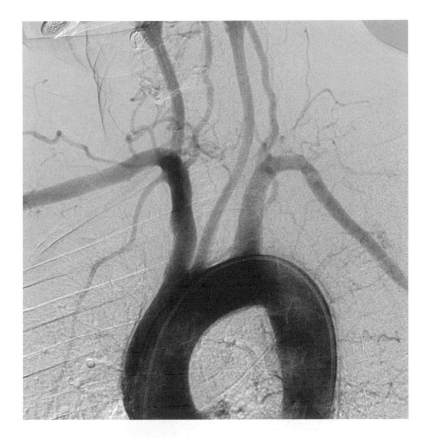

Fig. 16 _ Aortic Aortography (Spak, 2014).

2.3 Computer Tomography

The axial computer tomography with the use of contrast material (CTA) is the most common method for the imaging of the aorta. It offers a fast and an exact assessment of the aorta in relation to the size, the extent, and the localisation of the disease. It shows the affected sites of the aorta with atherosclerosis and differentiates the true lumen from the mural thrombus (Gotway, 2000; Fig. 17). In the cases of large aneurysms with the presence of intraluminal thrombus, it allows its exact evaluation. The reconstruction of the computer images (software) gives a perfect image of extent and the size of the pathologic state (Fig. 18) (Sabol, 2014).

In addition, 3D imaging of the aorta offers a good image of the extent of the disase. In the ideal case, the whole aorta, thoracic and abdominal must be examined on the same time. The main disadvantage of the CTA is the use of the contrast material, which can be a contraindication in patients with chronic renal failure or in patients allergic to the contrast material.

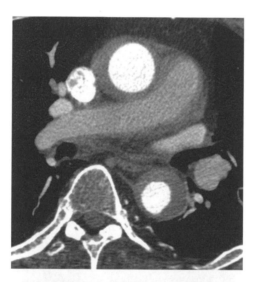

Fig. 17 _ CTA of an Aortic Aneurysm with the presence of a thrombus (Spak, 2014).

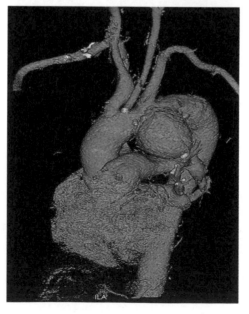

Fig. 18 _ CTA reconstuction of an aneurysm of the aortic arch (Sabol et al, 2014).

2.4 Intravascular Ultrasound

It is a dynamic examination with the use of a catheter designed for the diagnosis of the aortic wall and intimal flap in patients with the suspicion of the aortic dissection. It is suitable for the determination of the proximal and distal part of the dissection and for the identification of the true and false lumen of the aorta and for non-clear or controversial findings during aortography. Also, it offers the possibility for the diagnosis of intramural hematoma (IMH) and the penetrating atherosclerotic aortic ulcer (PAU). In cases of acute diseases of the aorta it is not the first line imaging modality due to time and professional demands.

2.5 Magnetic Resonance Imaging

The advantage of the magnetic resonance or of the new contrast-enhanced MRA comparing to the CTA is the possibility to image circumferencial and antero-posterior layers parallel to the median line, the possibility

Fig. 19 _ MRI of an Aaneurysm of the Ascending Aorta and the Aortic Arch (Cohn, 2011).

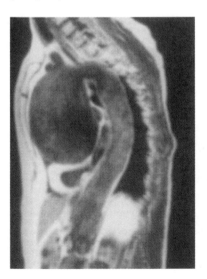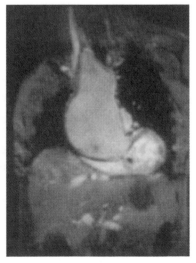

to avoid the use of the contrast material followed by the radiation of the patient.

Based on one examination it offers the possibility to consider the condition and the contractile function of the myocardium, and the anatomy of the heart valves and the coronary arteries. The contrast material (contrast-enhanced MRA) offers the possibility of the detailed imaging of the aorta and its branches and quality pictures comparable with the standard conventional aortography (Cohn, 2011). Despite its distinct advantages MRA is not an advanced examination method. The contraindications of the MRI is the presence of an iron magnetic material and the high probability for possible artifacts (till 64%), which demands the presence of experienced radiologic experts (Cohn, 2011).

Medical teams from the USA (Stanford) and Sweden (Linkoping) by means of 3D-MRI imaging with real time analysis found the blood flow velocity in healthy individuals and patients who underwent a valve sparing aortic root reconstruction operation according to two or three David's modifications: David I (tubular graft prosthesis), David V (Valsalva graft prosthesis or alternative two tubular prostheses). The primary result was the creation of turbulent flow (Markl et al., 2005; Kvitting, 2004; Fig. 20).

Creation of turbulent flow

The results in healthy individuals showed that during the contraction the existence of the turbulent flow has an extraordinary importance for the coronary Valsalva sinuses unlike the non-coronary sinus where it observed a spiral flow only in four out of ten individuals.

These observations are different from the observations of the Swedish team (Linkoping) which were done a year earlier, where a spiral flow was found in all three aortic sinuses and in six healthy individuals even increased spiral flow in the non-coronary sinus and in the right ventricle. In the contrary, the medical team from the USA (Stanford) found increased spiral flow only in the right and left coronary Valsalva sinuses.

During the final phase of the systolic period the turbulent flow is propagated and gradually takes the most part of the aortic surface and the main area of the linear flow from the ventricle is decreased. This flow lasts until the beginning of the diastolic phase. The direction of the flow is from the top down, lengthwise the lateral wall of the ventricle and continues towards the centre of the aorta (valve) at the ventricle bases. This flow develops an internal pressure to the valve leaflets and facilitates the aortic valve closure.

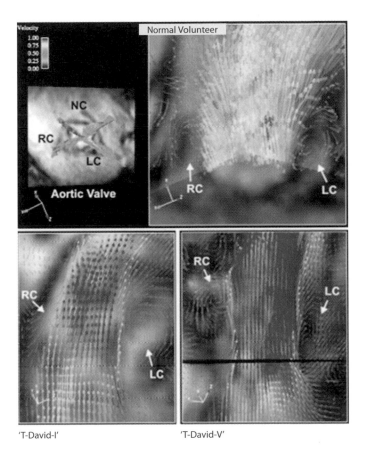

'T-David-I'   'T-David-V'

Fig. 20 _ 3D-MRI examination in two 2D imaging of the flow in the ascending aorta in healthy individuals (above) and in patients after David-I (left down) and David-V (right down) reimplantation of the aortic valve. The sections were done through an open aortic valve (left above) for the representation of the velocity of the blood flow in the left and right coronary leaflet. The creation of the so-called flow vortex is seen in all the cases (arrows) (Markl et al., 2005; Kvitting et al., 2004).

In patients after surgery (reimplantation according to David) there was no significant change in the turbulent flow behind the coronary valve leaflets, regardless whether it used a linear tubular or Valsalva prosthesis. However, the flow formation can be strengthened with the creation of neo-sinuses. The turbulent flow was observed to a lesser degree after proce-dures where tubular prostheses (without neosinuses) were used.

The result was slightly surprising; it seems that the creation of a turbu-lent flow during the systole is not the main result of the mechanic and geometric properties of the Valsalva sinuses, but rather it is associated with the hemodynamic conditions.

The medical team from the Linkoping did not observe any turbulent flow in two patients after the implantation of a tubular vascular prosthesis (David –I), on the contrary the medical team from Stanford in four patients after David –I observed a turbulent flow. This difference can be explained by the non-uniform way of measurements. The complete and rapid aortic valve closure decreases the tension on the aortic valve leaflets.

According to the team from Linkoping, the loss of this mechanism, and the loss of the "tension and relaxation" mechanism of the aortic root after the David-I procedure leads to the increase tension on the aortic valve leaflets and causes fibrosis, calcification, and earlier degeneration of the valve.

3.

Aortic Aneurysm

The aortic aneurysm belongs to the most common and most severe diseases of the aorta. Changes in the main artery that transports the blood
from the heart to the whole body could have lethal consequences for life.
In patients who are affected by an aortic aneurysm there is a 50% mortality rate, the other 50% receives an early diagnosis and surgical therapy.
From this point of view, we consider this disease to be very dangerous and
unpredictable.

3.1 Definition and classification of aortic aneurysms

With the disease entity – "true aortic aneurysm" we understand a permanent localised dilatation of the aorta with a diametree 50% larger than
standard diametre in the population. The aortic wall contains all the aortic
wall layers (intima, media, and adventitia). The wall of the false aneurysm
(pseudoaneurysm) does not contain all three aortic layers. We talk about
a cavity formed by the surrounding aortic tissue, with which it is connected
by a neck. The aortic aneurysm is the 13th most common cause of death in
the USA. In the normal population its occurrence is 5.9 times in one million
people every year. In men an aneurysm is most often diagnosed at an earlier age than in women (Cohn, 2011).

The standard risk factors for predisposition include smoking, arterial
hypertension (mainly non-treated) atherosclerosis and genetic anomalies,
for example, Marfan syndrome, Ehlers-Danlos syndrome, and the Bicus-
pid/Unicuspid aortic valve, in which the common characteristic is the abnormal structure of the aortic wall (see chapter 3.3).

In the past, some aortic aneurysms of the thoracic aorta were called
atherosclerotic aneurysms. Atherosclerosis of the vessels and aneurysms
of the thoracic aorta have common predisposition factors and usually exist
together. The aortic aneurysm is the result of the cystic medial necrosis of
the aorta at an older age, which offers a fertile ground for the development
of secondary atherosclerosis in the aneurysmatic wall. A brief overview of
the categorisation, classification, clinical signs, and diagnostic approaches
are shown in tables 4a, 4b, and 4c.

CLASSIFICATION (A)	• True Aortic Aneurysm • False Aortic Aneurysm (Pseudoaneurysm) • Chronic Aortic Dissection • Penetrating Aortic Atherosclerotic Ulcus
LOCATION	• Anuloaortic Ectasia (Asc. Aorta and Aortic Root) Ascending Aorta (above the sinotubular junction) • Aortic Arch • Descending Aorta • Abdominal or thoracoabdominal Aneurysm (Tab. 4c)

CLINICAL SYMPTOMS	• Asymptomatic
	• Symptomatic (according the Aneurysm location)
	  – Symptoms from the Aortic Regurgitation
	  – Pressure Pain (retrosternal, between scapulae, epigastric)
	  – Symptoms from the pressure on the surrounding organs (superior vena cava syndrome, dyspnea)-pressure on the trachea, pressure on laryngeal recurrent nerve, etc.

DIAGNOSTIC METHODS	• Echocardiographic examination • Computer Tomography with contrast material • Magnetic Resonace Imaging • Aortography and IVUS (less frequent) • Positrone Emission Tomography with CTA (Infectious Aneurysms)

Tab. 4a _ Basic division, classification, clinical signs, diagnostic modalities

CLASSIFICATION	• Congenital Aneurysm (Marfan syndrome, etc.) • Degenerative Aneurysm (cystic degeneration of the media, atherosclerosis, arterial hypertension) • Chronic postraumatic Aneurysm • Infectious Aneurysm • Aneurysm at the Anastomosis site • Post-stenotic Aneurysm (Aortic Valve stenosis)

Tab. 4b _ Classification of the Aneurysm according the etiology
(Nienaber et al., 2009).

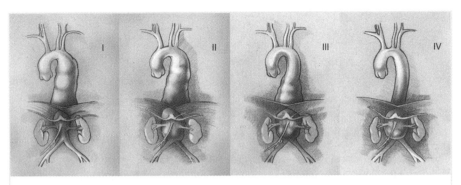

Type I:	The aneurysm involves the most part of the descending aorta and the upper part of the abdominal aorta
Type II:	The aneurysm involves the most part of the descending aorta and the subrenal abdominal aorta
Type III:	The aneurysm involves the distal half or the least part of the descending aorta and some part of the abdominal aorta
Type IV:	The aneurysm involves the most part of the abdominal aorta or the whole abdominal aorta

Tab. 4c _ Crawford Classification for the Thoracoabdominal Aneurysm

Brief overview of the aneurysm forms on the basis of the etiology:

1. True Aneurysms

This is the most common type of aortic aneurysm that needs a surgical intervention. Here do not belong the false aneurysms. From the whole arterial system, the aorta is most affected in 80% of all cases. The most often cause is the atherosclerosis (90%). The shape of the aneurysm (cavity) is saccular or fusiform.

2. Aneurysms associated with congenital disorders of the connective tissue

The most common congenital etiology for aortic aneurysm is the Marfan syndrome and many others (see chapter 3.2.2; Kainulainen et al., 1990).

3. Aneurysm of infectious etiology

Aortic aneurysms due to a specific infectious process are rare. If it develops, it is usually due to the secondary infection of an atherosclerotic plaque of the aortic intima. The symptomatology tends to be symptoms of native/prosthetic valve endocarditis (Chan et al., 1989).

4. Aneurysm of autoimmune etiology (non-infectious inflammatory aneurysm)

Takayasu arteritis and other diseases (see chapter 3.3.3) can cause dilatation of the aortic root which the synchronously dilatation of the aortic annulus may cause aortic valve regurgitation which can require surgical intervention (Piler et al., 2008).

5. Aneurysm of degenerative etiology

Cystic degeneration of the medial aortic wall (pathologically incorrect but used term medionecrosis) is the most common finding of the autopsy and biopsy specimens (after aortic wall excision during surgical aortic replacement). When discussing, anuloartic ectasia, this type of aneurysm most commonly affects the proximal part of the ascending aorta and the aortic root. The most common causes for degenerative aneurysm is the atherosclerotic process and untreated high blood pressure (Piler et al., 2008).

6. Chronic posttraumatic aneurysm

The most common mechanism for the development of an aneurysm is deceleration (fall from a height or motor vehicle accident). Predilection localisation is the proximal part of the descending aorta, at the attachment site of the ligamentum arteriosum. Either is treated with an urgent invasive procedure (endovascular treatment, surgical treatment), or in the case of exsaqvination leading to death. Sometimes the adventitia of the aorta is strong enough and the process passes to the chronic state, when it develops a chronic aneurysm (the accurate term – pseudoaneurysm), when the wall of the cavity is not formed by all the layers of the aortic wall (Cohn, 2011).

7. Post-stenotic aneurysm

Dilatation of the proximal part of the ascending aorta can be developed during the aortic valve stenosis, more often if the stenosis has a hereditary etiology (bicuspid/unicuspid valve; Cohn, 2011).

8. Pseudoaneurysm

On the contrary from the true aneurysm, in the pseudoaneurysm the wall is not formed from all the aortic layers. Most often the wall is formed by the adventitia and the surrounding tissue. The most common causes are the trauma, post-inflammatory changes, diagnostic catheterisation, and other (Cohn, 2011).

9. Chronic aortic dissection

During the acute aortic dissection there is through an entry (aortic intimal rupture) a flow of blood into the aortic wall with the consequence of the creation of a false aortic lumen. Fourteen days after the acute dissection, there is a chronic state. In the cases that the false lumen is not thrombotic and the flow is preserved, after some time may develop a chronic aneurysm (pseudoaneurysm), more often in the thoraco-abdominal aorta (Piler et al., 2008).

10. Penetrating atherosclerotic aortic ulcer (PAU)

The atherosclerotic plaque on the aortic wall may disturb the integrity of the wall and cause a range of potential complications, such as dissection, aneurysm, intramural hematoma, rupture or peripheral embolization of atherosclerotic particles. Most often it is localised on the abdominal aorta (Cohn, 2011).

11. Intramural hematoma (IMH)

Like the PAU, the IMH is considered as a precursor of aortic dissection. IMH belongs among the acute aortic diseases, which threaten the life of the patient, especially if it is localised on the ascending aorta. Different from the acute dissection, it has received less attention in scientific literature and clinical practise (Elefteriades, 2007).

3.2 Pathophysiology of the aortic aneurysm

The aortic media is responsible for the compliance and flexibility of the aorta (see chapter 1.2). At the aneurysm in the aortic media there is a disruption of the elastic fibers and a decrease in the amount of smooth muscle cells. As a result of this change is the development of microcystic areas in the aortic media and later necrosis of the media. During the systolic period of the cardiac cycle, the aorta (mainly the ascending aorta) expands and converts an amount of kinetic energy formed during the contraction of the left ventricle into potential energy of the aortic wall. During the diastolic period, the aortic wall "comes back" (we evidence a decrease in the aortic diametre) and the wall energy is converted back into kinetic energy of the antegrade flow. According to the Laplace law, the aortic dilatation causes an increase in wall tension, which in addition gradually gets thinner (Cohn, 2011). Ultimately it may lead to aortic insufficiency and to an increased predisposition to dissection or rupture of the aortic wall.

The development of a true aneurysm is a creeping pathological condition. The thoracic aorta expands very slowly, and its expansion depends on many factors. Elefteriades et al. report that the annual increase of the aortic diametre is in the range of 0.1cm/year in the cases of small aneurysms (<4cm) to 0.19mm/year for a larger aneurysm (>8cm) (Fig. 21ab). The authors also claim that a dissected aorta increases its diametre faster than a non-dissected and also a descending aortic aneurysm grows faster than an ascending aortic aneurysm (Fig. 21b; Tab. 5; Elefteriades, 2007).

Elefteriades et al. further demonstrated that the lesser body surface area, the higher incidence of complications like the rupture, the aneurysm dissection or death. For a precise calculation of the potential risk of an aortic aneurysm, the authors created a new variable called the aortic size index (ASI). The ASI is the result of the evaluation of two variables: the diametre of the aortic aneurysm and the BSA. The ASI is the aortic diametre relative to the BSA. Also, the authors report that on the basis of different analyses the ASI is a better predictor for potential complications than the maximal aortic aneurysm dimension.

On the basis of ASI, it is possible to stratify the patients and divide them into three risk categories (Fig. 22). Patients with an ASI<2.75cm/m² express a low risk for rupture or dissection, with the annual incidence of the above complications approximately 2.5%. Patients with an ASI in the range of 2.75 to 4.25cm/m² have a moderate risk with an annual incidence around 10%. Finally, patients with an ASI>4.25cm/m² have an annual risk of rupture, dissection, or death in the range of 30% to 40% (Davies et al., 2006).

Bonser et al. studied clinical and clinical-anatomic factors that affect the growth of the diametre of the thoracic aorta. The rate of the aortic expan-

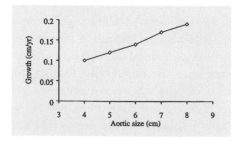

Fig. 21a _ Annual rate of growth of the aortic aneurysm relative to the aneurysm diametre (Elefteriades, 2007).

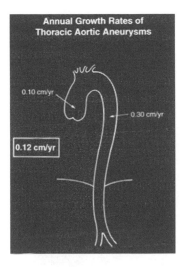

Fig. 21b _ Annual rate of growth of the aortic aneurysm relative to the localisation of the aneurysm (Elefteriades, 2007).

sion is proportion with the initial diametre of the aneurysm (Fig. 23). The size of the expansion of a degenerative aneurysm has a direct link with the amnatomic localisation of the aneurysm. The aneurysms of the descending aorta have a faster expansion in comparison with the proximal dilated aortic segments regardless of the initial diametre of the aneurysm. The aneurysms of the ascending aorta have a slower growth, regardless of the fact that they have a larger initial diametre (Bonser et al., 2000). The authors found a relationship between the existence of a thrombus in the lumen and a later progression of the diametre of the aortic aneurysm. It is surprising

Patient category	<4.0 cm (n=84)	4.0–4.9 cm (n=220)	5.0–5.9 cm (n=106)	6.0–6.9 cm (n=42)	7.0–7.9 cm (n=19)	>8.0 cm (n=7)	5.0 cm (sample mean)
All (n=478)	0.12 cm/yr (0.09–0.14)	0.16 cm/yr (0.13–0.18)	0.19 cm/yr (0.15–0.24)	0.21 cm/yr (0.10–0.32)	0.24 cm/yr (−0.06–0.55)	0.40 cm/yr (−0.18–1.02)	0.16 cm/yr (0.15–0.18)
Dissection status							
Chronic dissection (n=123)	0.12 cm/yr (0.07–0.17)	0.20 cm/yr (0.14–0.27)	0.25 cm/yr (0.10–0.43)	0.83 cm/yr (0.57–1.10)	0.08 cm/yr (−0.16–0.34)	N/A	0.21 cm/yr (0.17–0.25)
No dissection (n=355)	0.11 cm/yr (0.08–0.15)	0.14 cm/yr (0.11–0.17)	0.18 cm/yr (0.14–0.23)	0.15 cm/yr (0.04–0.27)	0.71 cm/yr (−0.04–1.55)	0.39 cm/yr (−0.13–0.94)	0.15 cm/yr (0.13–0.17)
Location of aneurysm							
Ascending or Arch (n=358)	0.12 cm/yr (0.08–0.14)	0.14 cm/yr (0.11–0.17)	0.18 cm/yr (0.12–0.22)	0.52 cm/yr (0.33–0.73)	0.18 cm/yr (−0.19–0.57)	N/A	0.15 cm/yr (0.13–0.17)
Descending or TA (n=120)	0.10 cm/yr (0.00–0.21)	0.20 cm/yr (0.13–0.27)	0.24 cm/yr (0.14–0.34)	0.13 cm/yr (−0.02–0.28)	0.98 cm/yr (0.24–1.78)	0.41 cm/yr (−0.32–1.20)	0.21 cm/yr (0.16–0.26)

Tab. 5 _ Growth of the Aneurysm diametre in dependence on existence of Dissection and location of the Aneurysm. (Elefteriades, 2007).

that this rising trend was not observed in cases in the presence of dissection or atherosclerotic involvement of the aorta, as stated for example by Elefteriades et al. (Fig. 24).

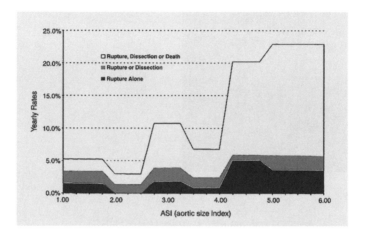

Fig. 22 _ The average annual incidence of aortic aneurysm complications (dissection, rupture, death). The diagram shows the risk incidence during the period of the first five years from the manifestation of the disease (Elefteriades, 2007).

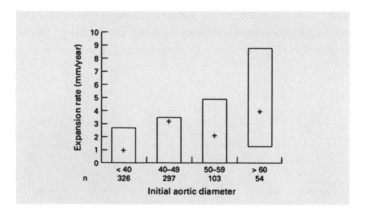

Fig. 23 _ The rate of the aneurysm growth according to the initial diametre p<0.001 (Kruskal-Wallis). Aortic segments with an initial diametre of >-60mm expand on average 4mm/year, in the meantime aneurysms (<50mm) expand on average 1.33mm/year (p<0.01) n=number of the aortic segments that were measured (for example asc. and desc. Aorta, aortic arch, aorta below the hiatus aorticus and so on; Bonser et al., 2000).

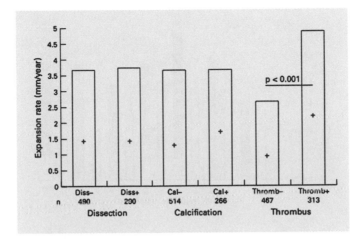

Fig. 24 _ Comparison of the rate of aneurysm expansion in case presence (+) and absence (-) of intraluminal thrombus, dissection and atherosclerotic disease of the aorta for all the examined aortic segments. The existence of a thrombus is related with a significant higher growth rate of the aneurysm (p<0.01; Bonser et al., 2000).

According to the authors' findings, the impact of the thrombus had an identical effect in all the aortic segments and at the same time leads to the growth of the diametree of the aneurysm depending on the initial dimension of the aneurysm (Fig. 25).

The authors believe that the thrombus potentiates the expansion of the aneurysm for the following three reasons:

- clinical observations suggest that the aortic wall where there is a mural thrombus is usually thinner than the aortic wall without a mural thrombus, and therefore there may be more pot ential loaded tension on the true aortic wall (Uemura et al., 1996). According to the Laplace law (T=P x r/2 t; T-tension on the aortic wall, p-distention presuure on the aortic wall, r-aortic diametre, t-thickness of the aortic wall), it can be argued that the thinning of the aortic wall leads to an increased tension on the aortic wall and therefore to aneurysm expansion;
- the aortic wall with a mural thrombus may be inherently weaker than the aortic wall with the same thickness without a thrombus;
- the thrombus is usually found in tortuous and large volume segments of the aorta, its creation may be the result of the decreased velocity of

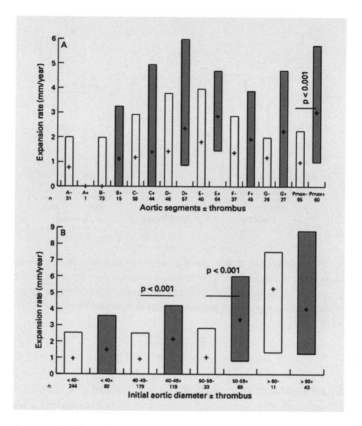

Fig. 25 _ (A) The effect of the thrombus on the rate of the aneurysm expansion depending on the aortic segment (individual letters indicate the aortic anatomic localisation, beginning from the ascending aorta and ending at the aortic area at the level of the origin of the mesenteric artery). It is shown the effect of the thrombus on the aneurysm expansion in all the segments. (B) The impact of the thrombus on the aneurysm growth is proportional to the initial aneurysm diametre. N=number of measured aortic segments (Bonser et al., 2000).

the blood flow and the relative blood stasis and after the measurement of the initial diametre is underestimated.

Elefteriades et al. presuppose that the risk of rupture or dissection of the aorta (critical point) occurs at the aneurysm size ≥60mm for the aneurysms of the ascending aorta and in the case of the descending aorta is ≥70mm (Elefteriades, 2002, 2007, Fig. 26).

Surgical (alternatively endovascular) intervention would be performed earlier than the aneurysm diametre when it reaches the above dimensions.

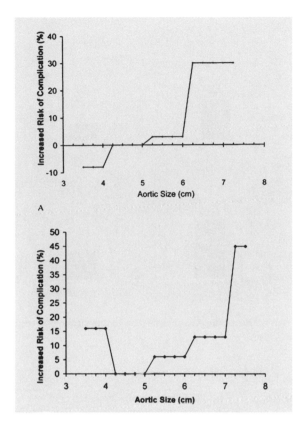

Fig. 26 _ Complications risk of aortic aneurysms (dissection, rupture, death) in relation to its diametre. The upper part of the diagram shows the risk for the ascending aorta, lower part for the descending aorta (Elefteriades, 2007)

The annual incidence (in %) of potential complications of the aortic aneurysm relative to the aortic diametre is captured in figure 27 (Elefteriades, 2007).

Coady et al. developed, on the basis of many observations, the indications criteria for preventive surgical intervention in cases of asymptomatic aortic aneurysms. The recommendations (tab. 6) involve also symptomatic patients (Coady et al., 1999b). This criteria is identical to the recommendations from the Yale Center for Thoracic Aortic Diseases, USA.

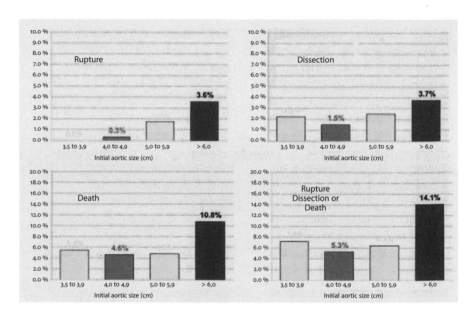

Fig. 27 _ Complications risk of the Aortic Aneurysms (dissection, rupture, death) in relation to its diametre (Elefteriades, 2007).

1.	Aortic Aneurysm Rupture		
2.	Symptomatic patient	a) Persistent pain after exclusion of other causes b) Pressure on the surrounding organs (trachea, esophagus, left main bronchus) c) Aortic Aneurysm combined with Severe Aortic Regurgitation	
3.	Absolute Diametre of the Aortic Aneurysm	Patient with Marfan syndrome (MFS)	Patient without MFS
	Ascending Aorta	4.5cm	5.5cm
	Descending Aorta	5.5cm	6.5cm
4.	Rate of growth of the aortic aneurysm a) growth ≥0.5cm/year or rapid progression relative to the absolute size (patient with MFS) b) growth ≥1.0cm/year or rapid progression relative to the absolute size (patient with MFS)		
5.	Acute Aortic Dissection a) ascending aorta-urgent surgical intervention b) descending aorta-individual management (complications and so on)		

Tab. 6 _ Recommended surgical indications criteria for Aortic Aneurysms. The criteria for MFS patients may also be applied in patients without MFS, but that have a family history for aortic disease other than the MFS (Elefteriades, 2007).

Pathophysiologic events that lead to the development of aortic aneurysms

1.   Remodelling of the aortic wall

The cystic medial degeneration is the anatomic background of the aneurysm. It is a non-specific degenerative state of the media layer, which is presented in different clinical conditions of the aorta, for example the idiopathic aneurysm, vascular collagen syndromes (Marfan syndrome, Ehlers-Danlos syndrome and other), chronic consequences of hypertension and ageing. Medial necrosis is characterised by the fragmentation of the elastic fibers, increased content of collagen, destruction of the leiomyocytes, and increased content of the basophilic mucopolysacharide matrix. These changes are more significant in the aortic aneurysms. There was no observed difference between the idiopathic forms of aneurysms and patients with Marfan syndrome. In the case of the aneurysm of the ascending aorta, which is associated with a bicuspid aortic valve, the results are inconsistent; some authors did post degenerative changes.

The histologic changes are evaluated on the basis of the criteria of Schlatmann and Becker (Agozzino et al., 2002)

1. degree (mild) (Fig. 28)
2. degree (intermediate)
3. degree (severe) (Fig. 29)

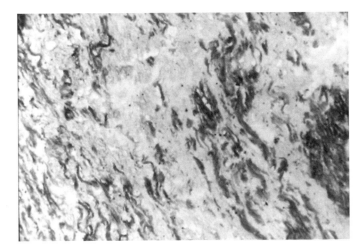

Fig. 28 _ Aortic wall from a patient with a mild degree of medionecrosis (Agozzino et al., 2002).

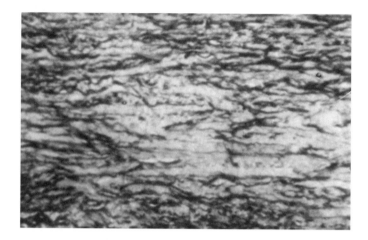

Fig. 29 _ Aortic wall from a patient with a severe degree of medione-crosis (Agozzino et al., 2002).

The study of Agozzino et al. (2002), showed that medial degeneration is not the same in the whole length of the ascending aorta. According to the authors, the larger and the most severe histologic changes (cystic necrosis) are found at the non-coronary sinus aortic site in patients with aortic valve disease and dilatation of the ascending aorta.

Two pathogenetic hypotheses may explain the above findings. The genetic ground of the damaged elastic tissue, which is a part of the connective tissue, causes aortic root and aortic annulus dilatation in the shape of a pear. The second hypothesis is the stronger hemodynamic force that act on the right side of the aortic wall above the non-coronary sinus of the aortic root.

Another study by the authors Tang et al. confirmed the hyperplastic cell arrangement in the media of the aneurysmatic ascending aorta. Their conclusions are:

a) despite the fact that the tunica media is getting thinner with the aneurysm growth, the real mass of the tunica media is increased;

b) the density of the leiomycytes in the media is constant, which means that the total number of the leiomyocytes is increased;

c) the leiomyocytes are the cell that are responsible for the vascular structure, because they produce the proteins of the intercellular matrix, like the metalloproteins (MMPs) and their regulators. The increased destruction of the elastin is probably the result of the increased concentration and activity of MMP-9. The destruction of elastin in the media is associated with the growth of the size of the aneurysm and it is directed from the lamina interna to the lamina externa (Tang et al., 2005).

2. Destruction of the extracellular matrix

As we mentioned above, the changes which are seen in the media are connected with the destruction of the connective tissue from the action of the proteinolytic MMPs (Wilton et, al, 2008; Ikonomides et al., 2004). The best studied group of enzymes are the MMPs of the intercellular matrix. Their action is precisely controlled at the level of the genetic expression with the activation of the proenzymatic forms of the MMPs and the inhibition of the specialised endogenous inhibitors (TIMPs)

In Koullias' study (Koullias et al., 2004), 30 patients showed increased levels of MMP-1 and MMP-2 in the aneurysms of the thoracic aorta (Fig. 30). On the contrary, the levels of MMP-2 were not significantly different from the measurements of the control group. In patients with aortic dissection a significant increased expressions of MMP-2 and MMP-9 compared to the patients without an aortic aneurysm was found (Fig. 31, 32, 33).

At the same time, the concentration of TIMP-1 and TIMP-2 in the tissue is significantly different from the concentration of the inhibitors in the test

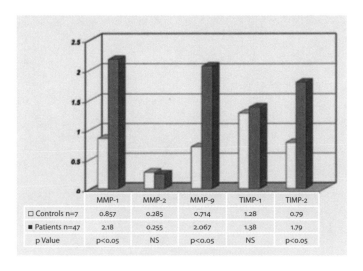

	MMP-1	MMP-2	MMP-9	TIMP-1	TIMP-2
☐ Controls n=7	0.857	0.285	0.714	1.28	0.79
■ Patients n=47	2.18	0.255	2.067	1.38	1.79
p Value	p<0.05	NS	p<0.05	NS	p<0.05

Fig. 30 _ Levels of MMPs and TIMPs in the aneurysm of the abdominal aorta (Koullias et al., 2004).

sample. An important finding is the fact that the ratio of MMP-9/TIMP-1 was significantly increased, which suggests a shift towards the proteinolysis in the aneurysm of the ascending aorta.

In the study by LeMaire et al.,15 patients with an aneurysm of the ascending aorta observed increased levels of MMP-9 and no difference at the levels of MMP-2 ,TIMP-1 and TIMP-2 (LeMaire et al., 2005). The importance and the significance of the role of MMP-9 in the support of the extracellular matrix are proven by the results of the study by Li Chen whose conclusion is that a polymorphism of the 8202A/G gene for MMP-9 is connected with the development of dissection and aneurysm of the thoracic aorta (Chen et al., 2006).

Many authors compared the association of MMPs between the idiopathic form of the aneurysm and the aneurysm that is associated with a bicuspid aortic valve. The conclusion concerning the importance of MMP-9 was very diverse and inconsistent. However when examining the importance of MMP-2, the results were similar, its concentration was higher in the aneurysma associated with a bicuspid aortic valve. The production of the MMP-9 may have an association with the inflammatory reaction because it exists in the neutrophils and the macrophages.

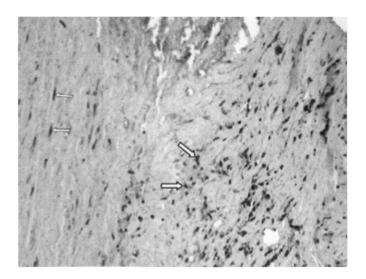

Fig. 31 _ Presence of MMP-1 in the cells in an aortic aneurysm (Koullias et al., 2004).

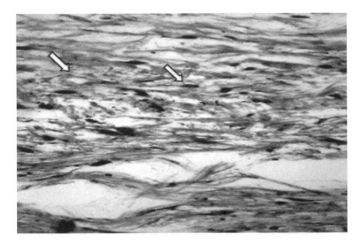

Fig. 32 _ Presence of MMP-1 in the cells in a dissection of the thoracic aorta (Koullias et al., 2004).

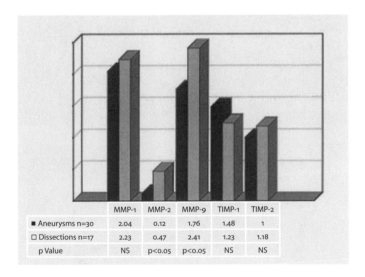

	MMP-1	MMP-2	MMP-9	TIMP-1	TIMP-2
■ Aneurysms n=30	2.04	0.12	1.76	1.48	1
□ Dissections n=17	2.23	0.47	2.41	1.23	1.18
p Value	NS	p<0.05	p<0.05	NS	NS

Fig. 33 _ Levels of MMPs and PIMPs in an aortic aneurysm and dissection (Koullias et al., 2004).

3. The decrease of the leiomyocytes

The decrease of the leiomyocytes in the media is found in the aortic wall samples of the aortic aneurysms (Fig. 34) (Kirsch et al., 2006). Schmid et al. found a 25% decrease of these cells in the nuclei in the comparison of an idiopathic aortic aneurysm and healthy aorta (Schmid et al., 2004). A significant decrease up to 32% was in the aneurysms associated with a bicuspid aortic valve. This may be caused by a programmed apoptosis of the cells that is activated by the receptors of cell death-Fas (CD95).

4. Inflammatory changes

Schown et al. showed an infiltration of macrophages, T-lymphocytes, in a smaller amount of B-lymphocytes and finally of natural killers cells in the

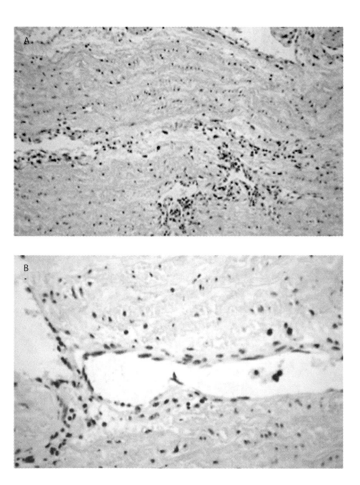

Fig. 34 _ Intima of idiopathic form of an aortic aneurysm (56mm), and a immunohistologic finding of macrophages with the use of antibodies labeled CD68 membrane receptors (Kirsch et al., 2006).

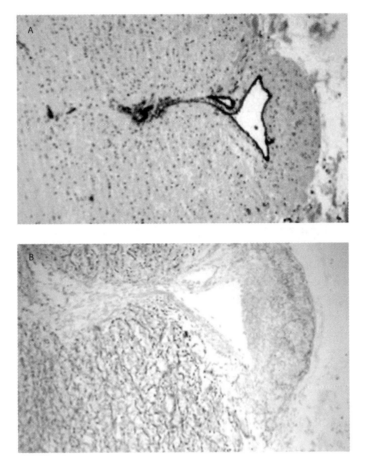

Fig. 35 _ Intima of idiopathic form of an aortic aneurysm (57mm), and a immunohistologic finding of macrophages with the use of antibodies labeled CD31
membrane receptors (Kirsch et al., 2006).

wall of the aortic aneurysm (Schmid et al., 2004). Other authors observed an
extensive infiltration of mononuclear cells in the adventitia and in the media of the aortic aneurysm.

5. Angiogenesis

Recently, the presence of newly formed vessels in the adventitia and media were observed in the aortic wall samples from an idiopathic aneurysm
form of the ascending aorta, while the cells that were connected with the

angiogenesis were the macrophages. Activated macrophages produce growth factors that cause migration and proliferation of the endothelial cells (Fig. 35). Also, they release and activate MMPs and serine protease and are engaged in the migration process of the endothelial cells during the angiogenesis. At the same time, the concentration of the neovascularisation and the macrophages was higher in the proximal part of the aneurysm than at the localisation of the largerst dilatation (Kirsch et al., 2006).

6. Biologic factors

a) Asymetry of the aortic root

The long axis of the left heart ventricle and the axis of the aortic root together create an angle of 140°-150°, which together with the 30°-40° axial curvature of the ascending aorta create a change in the blood flow, where the highest velocity of the blood flow is at the site of the non-coronary sinus and the flow rotation is counterclockwise. This blood flow asymmetry results in the exertion of different forces at particular sites of the aortic wall. The forces acting on the right and non-coronary sinus are 21% and 10% respectively higher than the forces acting on the left coronary sinus. This explains why the non-coronary sinus is larger, followed by the right and finally the left coronary sinus. This may have a connection with the reality why the aneurysms of the aortic root have the trend to be developed in the curvature of the aorta. This reality confirms the above mentioned claims that the degenerative destruction of the media is more severe on the right posterolateral site of the ascending aorta

b) Aortic dilatation

At the development of the aortic aneurysm, the increased pressure that act on the aortic wall (Laplace law), becomes a significant factor contributing to the progression of the dilatation of the aortic aneurysm and at the same time the risk for aortic rupture is increased. The increase of the pressure that acts on the aortic wall is proportional with the increase of the aortic diametre. Measurements showed that with the growth of the aortic aneurysm, the aortic compliance decreases. At a diametre of approximately 60mm, the aorta becomes a non-flexible tube (Fig. 36). The final result is that the aneurysmatic aortic wall during systole cannot stretch so the whole force of the heart contraction is converted into tension acting on the aortic wall. Also, it was confirmed that there is a direct relationship between the severity of the degenerative disease of the media and the aortic diametre (Elefteriades, 2007).

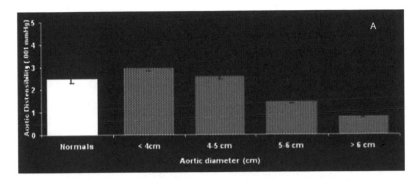

Fig. 36 _ The elasticity of the wall of a physiologic aorta the wall of the aortic aneurysm relative to the aortic diametre (Elefteriades, 2007).

c) Interaction between the aortic valve and the aortic root (circulus vitiosus)

The modification of the elastic properties of the sinuses of the Valsalva results in the exertion of more pressure on the aortic sinuses which results in the faster creation of inosis of flaps. On the contrary, the dilatation of the aortic root results in the loss of the coaptation line between the valve leaflets that lead to valve regurgitation. The dysfunction of the aortic valve results in abnormal blood flow that may contribute to the progression of the aortic wall disease. During the valve stenosis, the dilatation of the ascending aorta or of the aortic root is one of the first adaptation mechanisms for the decreased blood volume during systole and the dilatation of the

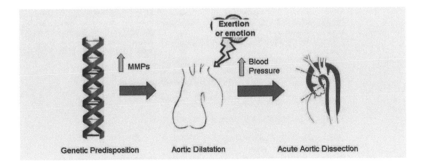

Fig. 37 _ Possible way for the development of complications in the aortic aneurysm – aortic dissection: high blood pressure is manifested usually during the winter months and early morning hours (Elefteriades, 2007).

ascending aorta does not progress as is in the case of regurgitation of the aortic valve. In the case of valve regurgitation, there is increased pressure along the ascending aorta due to the increased mobility of the aortic root. The localisation with the highest pressure is 20mm above the sinotubular junction (STJ). In the figure 37, it shows the pathophysiologic mechanism of complications in the aortic aneurysm and the aortic dissection.

7. Molecular genetics

Five percent of the known aneurysms of the thoracic aorta are developed in the ground of Marfan syndrome. The question is if the genetic anomalies can clarify the other 95% cases. According to the registry in Yale of 500 family trees of patients with aneurysm or dilatation of the thoracic aorta (patients with MFS were excluded), 21% of the patients had at least one family member with an aneurysm of the thoracic aorta. These patients with a positive family history have a higher predisposition in the dilatation of the aorta and the clinical picture is exhibited at an earlier age. Coady et al. confirmed that 19% of the patients with an aneurysm of the thoracic aorta

Array Probe ID	Primary Gene ID	Gene Symbol	Frequency in top 500 ranks among 500 bootstrap resampling	Expression in TAA
124958	56143	PCDHA5	0.82	Up
227481	374897	SBSN	0.82	Up
182618	hCG1773879.2		0.80	Up
219146	348932	SLC6A18	0.77	Up
211834	hCG1820398.1		0.77	Up
214799	219968	OR5B21	0.77	Up
619119	388751	LOC388751	0.76	Up
196612	22875	ENPP4	0.72	Up
213445	8809	IL18R1	0.72	Up
208499	283349	RASSF3	0.71	Up
410937	387695	C10orf99	0.71	Up
163657	8831	SYNGAP1	0.69	Up
183110	hCG2028451.1		0.65	Up
137330	hCG1820722.2		0.64	Up
141979	5998	RGS3	0.64	Up
115931	64100	ELSPBP1	0.63	Up
214599	29957	SLC25A24	0.60	Up
192269	6944	VPS72	0.96	Down
117989	3615	IMPDH2	0.93	Down
139001	3033	HADHSC	0.92	Down
206569	6631	SNRPC	0.88	Down
156536	5245	PHB	0.88	Down
125597	79001	VKORC1	0.87	Down
179149	3163	HMOX2	0.82	Down
179328	8607	RUVBL1	0.82	Down
162516	231	AKR1B1	0.78	Down
162516	231	AKR1B1	0.78	Down
201766	6184	RPN1	0.77	Down
115653	8721	EDF1	0.77	Down
185037	1019	CDK4	0.77	Down
178575	128240	APOA1BP	0.75	Down
154562	25764	HYPK	0.71	Down
175040	516	ATP5G1	0.68	Down
187195	29101	SSU72	0.67	Down
119963	10001	MED6	0.66	Down
232086	hCG2042278		0.65	Down
173844	4282	MIF	0.65	Down
180941	hCG1793363.2		0.62	Down
112601	79228	WDR58	0.62	Down
224173	83858	ATAD3B	0.61	Down
204089	51070	NOSIP	0.61	Down
178334	11164	NUDT5	0.59	Down

Tab. 7 _ A list of 41 genes, on the basis of an examination that can diagnose the risk for the development or the presence of an aortic aneurysm (Wang et al., 2007).

have a positive family history of an aneurysm of the thoracic aorta (Coady et al., 1999).

Changes in the fibrillin-1 gene were found also in patients without MFS and also many other changes were found in the genes of 3p24-25, 5q13-14, and 11q23-2-24 (Milewicz et al., 1996).

The form of inheritance is usually autosomal dominant, but was also observed in other forms of inheritance. The family members of the patients with an aneurysm of the ascending aorta have a higher risk for the development also of an aneurysm of the ascending aorta. The family members of the patients with an aneurysm of the descending aorta have a higher risk for the development of a thoracoabdominal aneurysm.

Yale University examined 30000 ways of expression (transcription) of RNA in the blood of patients with an aneurysm of the thoracic aorta and were then compared with samples from patients who do not have aortic aneurysm. It was found that with the examination of 41 genes (table 7) may well enough distinguish patients with aortic aneurysm or without, and this was only on the basis of a regular blood examination, where the sensitivity of this test is 80% (Wang et al., 2007).

3.3 Etiology of the aortic aneurysm

The etiological issues of the aortic aneurysm are very wide. In this subchapter we analyse the diseases that cause aortic aneurysm divided into these groups:

- aneurysm of a genetic etiology;
- aneurysm with positive family history (hereditary);
- aneurysm of non-infectious inflammatory etiology;
- aneurysm associated with arterial hypertension and atherosclerosis;
- aneurysm from infectious causes.

3.3.1. Aneurysms from a genetic etiology

"GenTAC" are the initials for the American archive for thoracic aortic aneurysm and cardiovascular diseases with a genetic background. The patients come from five regional research centres and from the year 2010, they number more than 2800. This archive contains collected clinical data and genetic biological samples. The purpose of this archive is to assist scientists in the diagnosis, treatment, and prevention of this form of aortic aneurysms.

The five regional centres are:

- John Hopkin's Medical University,
- Oregon Health and Science University,
- University of Pennsylvania,
- University of Texas Houston/Baylor College of Medicine,
- Weil Medical College University Cornell.

In the diagnostic groups are classified patients who have:

- Bicuspid aortic valve (BAV) with aortic coarctation at the aortic isthmus,
- BAV with positive family history,
- Ehlers-Danlos syndrome (EDS),
- Gene mutations (FBN, TGF BR 1, TGF BR 2, ACTA 2, MYH II),
- familial aneurysms of the thoracic aorta (Lujan-Frynl syndrome) and dilatation,
- Loyes-Dietz syndrome,
- Marfan syndrome,
- other aneurysms and aortic dilatations in patients younger than 50 years old,
- other heart defects,
- Shprintzen-Goldberg syndrome,
- Turner syndrome.

The Figure 38 shows the percentual expression of the surgical interventions according to each etiology of the aortic aneurysm.

The average age of the patients at the first surgical intervention in the case of BAV/coarctation was 15.3 years old. In the case of BAV with a positive family history, the average age was 43.4 years old. In the case of BAV without family history, the average age was 44.4 years old.

In patients with EDS the average age was 52.3 years old, overall age at the first surgical intervention in MFS was 34.3 years old, and in the case of LDS, it was 12.1 years old (Fig. 39) In the patients with MFS the number of surgical interventions (according to the type of the aneurysm) moves at the level of 50% at the aortic root replacement, 45% at the replacement of ascending aorta and at 30% at the reconstruction interventions of the aortic root. Under the margin of 10% are the isolated aortic interventions in the meaning of replacement or repair of the aortic valve without intervention on the aorta or aortic root.

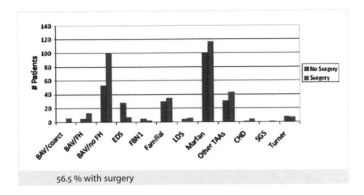

Fig. 38 _ Percentual expressions of the surgical interventions according to the etiology of the aortic aneurysm (GenTAC, 2008).

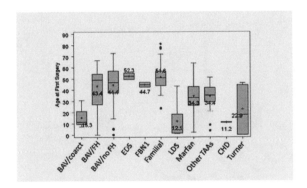

Fig. 39 _ The average age of the patients at the first surgical intervention (GenTAC, 2008).

In patients with BAV, 70% of the surgical operations are for replacement of the ascending aorta (supracoronary replacement), 45% are also for replacement of the aortic arch (partial, full) and less often replacement of the aortic root. In 10% of the cases, they achieve the isolated repairs of the aortic valve and 20% aortic valve replacement.

In the patients with a positive family history of an ascending aorta aneurysm the number of the supracoronary replacements of the aorta achieved is 55%, in 35% was for the replacement of the aortic root and in 25% of the cases replacement of the aortic arch and a reconstructive intervention on the aortic valve was performed (Fig. 40). The reasons for surgical interventions are shown in Figure 41.

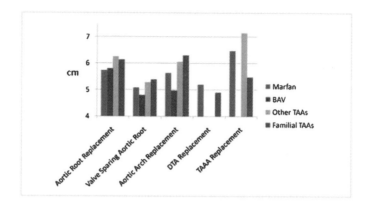

Fig. 40 _ The range of the surgical interventions (GenTAC, 2008).

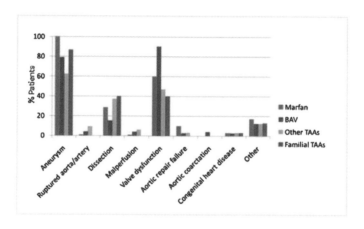

Fig. 41 _ The reasons for the surgical interventions (GenTAC, 2008).

The results of the GenTAC archive:

1. In the patients with MFS, with a positive family history of an ascending aortic aneurysm and in patients younger than 50 years old, was the aneurysm of the ascending aorta/aortic root with aortic valve regurgitation or without it the most common cause for surgical intervention. In the patients with BAV is observed more frequent sporadic prevalence of aortic valve dysfunction.

2. The proximal part of the aorta is the most common localisation for surgical interventions. After is the aortic root aneurysm, next the aneurysm

of the descending aorta and less frequently, it is a surgical intervention due to an aneurysm of the thoracoabdominal aorta.

3. There are mutual differences between the diagnostic groups, for example the patient's age at the first operation.

4. The purpose of the GenTAC is to optimise the therapeutic approach in each syndrome.

3.3.2 Aneurysms with positive family history (hereditary)

Albornoz and Coady studied the genetic trees of 3000 patients from the archive of the thoracic aorta from Yale University (Fig. 42).Family correlation was clear in 21.5% of 470 patients who were not affected by the Marfan syndrome. Males dominated in the family group (2.5:1) and it was less dominant in the group of patients affected by MFS (1.6:1).

Patients with MFS were in the time of the aortic aneurysm diagnosis younger than the group of patients with positive family aneurysm history (27.4 years old vs 55.4 years old), and were younger than the group of patients with a sporadic aortic aneurysm (58.2 years old vs 65.7 years old).

From 520 patients, in 413 cases (79.4%) had an aneurysm of the ascending and in 107 cases (20.6%) had an aneurysm of the descending aorta. In the group with a positive family history, 63 patients (79.7%) had aortic an-

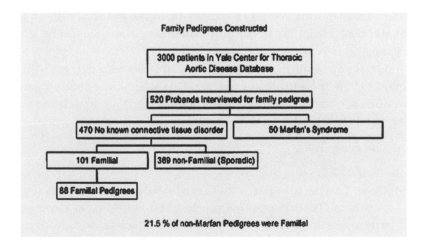

Fig. 42 _ Genealogical tree (Albornoz et al., 2006).

eurysm. Also, 22 patients with a pathology on the ascending aorta had in the half of the cases an aneurysm and on the other half had a dilatation of the aorty. In the group with sporadic aneurysm, 235 (82.1%) of the 287 cases had a pathologic finding on the ascending aorta, however aortic aneurysm existed in only 52 patients. In the group of patients with MFS, 41 patients (87.2%) from the total number of 47 cases had a pathologic aneurysm 74.4% and 6 patients (12.8%) had only a dilated aorta. Three patients with a finding on the descending aorta had this aortic segment dilated. The ratio of the dilatation of the ascending aorta was significant higher than the dilatation of the ascending aorta.

The rate of growth of the aneurysm was 0.21cm/year in the cases of an aneurysm positive family history, 0.16cm/year in the cases of sporadic aneurysm and 0.10cm/year in the patients with MFS.

In 79.5% of the patients (70 patients), there was a dominant hereditary form, 30 patients had an autosomal dominant type, 24 patients had an autosomal dominant type against a dominant heredity bound to the X-chromosome, and 15 patients had autosomal dominant type with a reduced penetration. In 20.5% of the patients (18 patients) had the form of heredity autosomal recessive, in the other cases there was a recessive heredity bound to the X-chromosome and autosomal recessive diseases. Individuals with a family history of an aneurysm of the ascending aorta have a higher risk for the development of an aortic aneurysm. Individuals with a positive history of an abdominal aortic aneurysm have a high probability for the development of an aneurysm on the descending aorta. In the patients with a positive family history of an aortic aneurysm, the history of the arterial hypertension occurred more frequently in the patients with an aneurysm of the descending aorta than in patients with an ascending aorta aneurysm (Albornoz et al., 2006; Coady et al., 1999b).

On the basis of the study by Kien and Hasham dealing with the gene mapping in the chromosomes, they showed that specific chromosomal regions are bonded to the familial (genealogy) aneurysm of the thoracic aorta (TAA/AD)

The genes were:

a) Gene TAAD1 5q13-q14;
b) Gene TAAD2 3q24-p25, which is a defective gene and is found in the region 25-CM between D3S3701 and D3S1211. Clinical symptoms are an aneurysm and dissection of the ascending aorta, aorta with a dominant type of heredity with a decreased penetration and the clinical symptoms are presented in different ages at the time of establishment of the

diagnosis. This region overlaps the region M7S2 like in the MFS. The phenotype of the patients and the complications in the cardiovascular and muscular system are similar with the MFS, but without evident visible signs;

c) Gene FAA1 11q232-924;

d) TAAD 16q12.2-p13.13 (at Botallo duct) in the region 20cm D165519-D165403.

Like in the MFS, it is the aortic rigidity in symptomatic and asymptomatic patients that is one of the first symptoms of the disease. An important role in the diagnosis is an examination with a MRI, where the aortic changes can be diagnosed. The aortic rigidity may partially be treated with beta blockers (Hasham et al., 2003).

These include:

1. Marfan syndrome (MFS)
2. Loyes-Dietz syndrome (LDS)
3. Turner syndrome (TS)
4. Alagille syndrome (AS)
5. Bicuspid aortic valve (BAV)
6. Ehlers-Danlos syndrome (EDS)
7. Sphrintzen-Goldberg syndrome (SGS)
8. Osteogenesis imperfect (OI)
9. Beal's syndrome-CCA
10. Polycystic kindey disease (PKD)
11. Nooman syndrome(NO)
12. Klippel-Feil syndrome (KFSo
13. Pseudoxanthoma elasticum (PxEo
14. Klinefert syndrome (KS)

3.3.2.1 Marfan syndrome

The incidence of the patients born with Marfan syndrome (MFS) is 1 in 9800. It is a disease with an autosomal dominant type of heredity, in which about 25% of the cases are found in the families sporadically. It affects many organs, including the skeleton, heart, vessels, eyes, and lungs. The classic Marfan syndrome is caused by a genetic mutation of the gene for the fibrilin-1 that is found on the chromosome 15q. The fibrilin-1 is a 350 KD glycoprotein that is synthetised by a precursor of glycoprotein 375KD, which is transported from the cell to the extracellular matrix. The extracellular matrix is vital for the structural integrity and function of the connective tissue, but also serves as a reservoir for rast factors. Fibrilin-1 is connected with other fibrilin molecules and other proteins and creates thin fibers called microfibers in the connective tissue, that provide strength for the LTBP-latent conjugated proteins of the transforming growth factor. The LTBP maintain the transforming growth factor beta (TGF-β) inactive. The changed fibrilin causes an excess of TGF-β that subsequently destroys the tissue. A failure in the interaction between fibrilin-1 and LTBPs results in the excessive stimulation of the factor TGF-β. As a result of the loss of the fibrilin-1's ability to bind calcium, there is a degeneration of the elastic fibers of the aortic wall, and gradually the interlamelar spaces are expanded, which varies the ratio between elastic and collagen fibers in favour of the collagen fibers that decreases the elasticity of the aortic wall. The abnormal fibrilin also causes an abnormal endothelial reaction in the intraluminar flow changes, the so-called mechanic-transduction. This stagnates the production of the nitric oxide from the endothelial cells. The result is an increase in the aor-

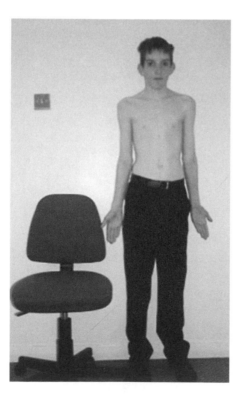

Fig. 43 _ A boy with MFS at the age of 12 years old (Dean, 2007).

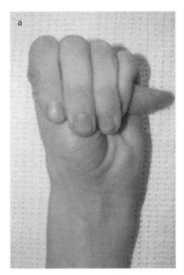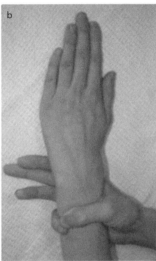

Fig. 44 _ Arachodactylia and hypermobility of the fingers in a patient
with MFS; positive thumb, wrist examination (Dean, 2007).

tic wall tension, so-called wall stress during the pulse wave. The mentioned
structural and functional changes in the aortic wall of the patients with
MFS markedly predispose them to the dilatation, development of an aneurysm, respectively aortic dissection, and aortic valve regurgitation. The
aorta dilates maximally in the growth period between 6-14 years old (Fig. 43),
the risk for dissection development becomes significant after 30 years old
(De Paepe et al., 1996).

A genetic mutation that causes a change in the protein cysteine (epi-
dermal growth factor) is associated with luxation of the eye lenses. Genetic
mutations in the central region (exons 24-25) that we call "neonatal region"
may be associated with the phenotype of the most severe degree of neonatal MFS to the sporadic luxation of the eye lenses. It is assumed that the
"mutated" fibrilin-1 does not fulfil enough of its mechanical function and
cannot keep the TGF-β under control, which causes an excess of TGF-β or
an increased of activity with pathological consequences in many body organs (Dean, 2007; Mulder, 2008).

Given the great variability of the clinical manifestations of MFS, its
diagnosis currently is being made according to the revised Ghent Nosology (Tab. 8) which includes manifestations localised in the skeleton, eyes,
cardiovascular system, lungs, skin, conjuctives, and the brain membranes.

System	Major criterion	Involvement
Skeletal	At least 4 of the following features: • Pectus carinatum • Pectus excavatum requiring surgery • ULSR <0.86 or span:height >1.05 • Wrist and thumb signs • Scoliosis >20° or spondylolisthesis • Reduced elbow extension (<170°) • Pes plenus • Protrusio acetabulae	2 of the major features, or 1 major feature and 2 of the following: • Pectus excavatum • Joint hypermobility • High palate with dental • Crowding • Characteristic face
Ocular	Lens dislocation (ectopia lentis)	Flat cornea Increased axial length of globe (causing myopia) Hypoplastic iris or ciliary muscle (causing decreased miosis)
Cardiovascular	Dilatation of the aortic root Dissection of the ascending aorta	Mitral valve prolapse Dilatation of the pulmonary artery, below age 40 Calcified mitral annulus, below age 40 Other dilatation or dissection of the aorta
Pulmonary	None	Spontaneous pneumothorax Apical blebs
Skin/Integument	None	Striae atrophicae Recurrent or incisional hernia
Dura	Lumbosacral dural ectasia	None
Genetic findings	Parent, child or sibling meets these criteria independently Fibrillin 1 mutation known to cause Marfan syndrome Inheritance of DNA marker haplotype linked to Marfan syndrome in the family	None

Tab. 8 _ Classification of MFS according the Ghent nosology (Dean, 2007).

In the main criteria for the establishment of the diagnosis MFS belongs the dilatation of the aortic root, aortic valve regurgitation, aortic dissection, lens ectopia, dural ectasia, and the erosion of the lumbosacral vertebrae caused by it (De Paepe et al., 1996).

In practice we recognised also the so-called partial forms of MFS, for example phenotype MASS-mitral-aortic-skin-skeletal with the affection of the mitral (prolapse) and aortic valve, skin, and skeleton.

The patients are usually tall, slim with long limbs, long fingers (arachodaktylia) (Fig. 44), have funnel shaped thorax, and also sometimes scoliosis. There other clinical signs, for example arcuate dururm with an excess number of teeth, wrinkled skin or spontaneous collapse of the lung parenchyma (De Paepe et al., 1996; Dean, 2007; Mulder, 2008).

Cardiovascular system and MFS

Cardiovascular complications that are caused in association with MFS, are the result of structural and functional changes in the aortic wall and significantly predispose to the dilatation and development of an aneurysm or directly to the dissection of the aorta and the regurgitation of the aortic valve. The so-called phenotype MASS includes affection of the mitral and aortic valve, the skin, and the skeleton.

The most frequent and most severe complication that is the cause for a high mortality and morbidity is the anulo-aortic ectasia associated with a central type of regurgitation of the aortic valve. With the diametre of the aorta approximately 5.0cm increases the risk for dissection, therefore the replacement of the ascending aorta is indicated even at the diametre of ≥ 4.5cm. That is why the early diagnosis of the aortic diametre (and the dynamic growth) is a verty important surgical indication criteria. They are investigated by the echocardiographic examination (Fig. 45), CTA examination, and MRI examination (Fig. 46) (Nataf et al., 2006, Dean, 2007).

The mortality of the complications of MFS decreased from 70% in the 1972 to 48% in 1998 and the average survival age increased from 32±16 in 1972 to 45±17 in 1998.

The aorta of a patient with MFS is characterised by the cystic degeneration of the media. This topic was explained in chapter 3.2.

The pharmacologic treatment (so called anti-impulse therapy) with beta-blockers and antihypertensives decrease the power of transmission of the heart contraction to the aortic wall in adult patients and also in pediatric patients. There is a decrease of the blood pressure and a decrease of

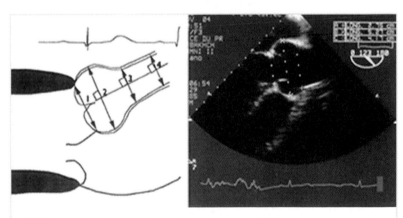

ECHO Echocardiographic dimensions of the aortic root at different levels (Nataf et al., 2006)

Left: 1) aortic root (internal diametre)
       2) sinuses of Valsalva (external diametre)
       3) sinotubular junction (external diametre)
       4) ascending aorta (external diametre)

Right: Transesophageal echocardiography of an aneurysm of the aortic root (Marfan syndrome) with anulo-aortic ectasia

Fig. 45 _ Graphic figure of an aortic root (left) and echocardiographic image of the aortic root (right) (Nataf et al., 2006).

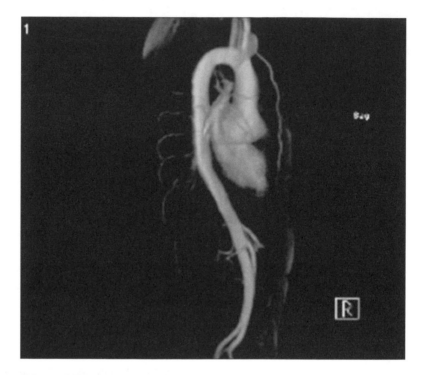

Fig. 46 _ MRI examination of an anulo-aortic ectasia in a patient with MFS
(Mulder, 2008).

the strain on the aortic wall. Also, the angiotensin II antagonists decrease
the progression of the growth of the aortic diametre and have a protective
effect on the elastic fibers of the aortic wall.

3.3.2.2 Loeys-Dietz syndrome

Loeys- Dietz syndrome (LDS) is a new syndrome that was first described in
2005. It is a disease of the connective tissue with an autosomal dominant
type of heredity that is caused by a mutation of the genes receptors one
and two beta transforming growth factor (TGF-β). The molecules of TGF-β
play a significant role in the embryogenesis of the cardiovascular system
and in the development of the ventral myocardium. Mutations of the gene
receptors TGF-β may significantly affect the function of the ventricular myocardium. In patients with LDS it has resulted in a failure in the function of

the left heart ventricle, hypokinesis of the ventricular septum, and an apex of the left heart ventricle (Aalberts et al., 2008).

The first type of LDS has a lot of common symptoms like MFS. For example, anulo-aortic ectasis, arachodactylia, dolichostenomelia (slim and tall person with long limbs), thoracic deformations, and hypermobility of the articulations. The second type of LDS has common symptoms like the vascular type of Ehlers-Danlos syndrome (EDS). The type LDS 1 has more aggressive consequences on the cardiovascular system than MFS has (Aalberts et al., 2008). The main clinical symptoms are shown in table 9.

The main symptoms, that differentiate patients with LDS from MFS is the hypertelorismus, clft of the palate, bifid hypertrophic uvula (Fig. 50), spiral arteries, craniosynostosis, Botallo duct, and a defect of the interventricular septum. Patients affected by the LDS type 2 have skin anomalies (a trend to the formation of bruises, transparent velvety skin), hypermobility of the articulation, and others.

In the Figure 47, it shows a female patient with LDS type 1 in which the classic craniofascial features are not developed. Figure 48 shows a young male patient with specific craniofascial features and on Figure 49 is the

	Marfan	LDS 1	LDS 2	EDS 4
Vascular				
Aortic aneurysm/dissection	++	+++	+++	+++
Tortuosity	-	+++	+++	-
ASD	-	+	+	-
Skeletal				
Arachnodactyly[a]	+++	++	++	-
Dolichostenomelia[b]	++	+		-
Pectus abnormalities	++	++	++	-
Joint laxity	++	++	+++	+ (Small joints)
Pes equinovarus[c]	-	+		+
Facial				'Old looking', deep-set eyes
Craniosynostosis[d]	-	+/++	-	-
Hypertelorism[e]	-	+++	-	-
Cleft palate/bifid uvula	-	+++	+ (Uvula)	-
Skin				
Excessive striae	+	-	-	-
Easy bruising	-	-	+++	++
Soft, velvety, translucent	-	+	++/+++	+++
Eyes				
Ectopia lentis[f]	++	-	-	-
Other				
Rupture large organs	-	-	+/++	++

The presence or absence of the features in italics might help to differentiate from Marfan syndrome. -infrequently, + around 25-50%, ++ around 50-75%, +++ >75%, [a] long slender fingers, [b] thin body habitus and long extremities, [c] clubfeet, [d] premature closure of cranial sutures, [e] increased distance between pupils, [f] lens subluxation.

Tab. 9 _ The main clinical features of MFS, LDS type 1, LDS type 2, and EDS type 4 (Aalberts et al., 2008).

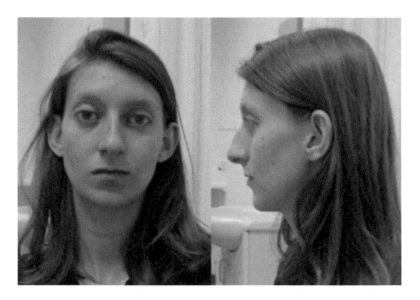

Fig. 47 _ Female patient affected by LDS type 1, who does not have the characteristic craniofascial features (Aalberts et al, 2008).

left lower limb of the same patient. Patients affected by the LDS type 1 are forced to undergo ca ardiac surgery operation in the early period and have a shorter lifespan than patients with the second type LDS.

The cardiovascular disability usually is very severe, so regular echocardiographic controls are necessary. Special attention needs to be given to the size of the aortic root and the rate of its expansion. It is also right to do an echocardiography control of the pulmonary artery (Fig. 51).

In patients with LDS requires a CTA examination of the whole arterial system in order to exclude an aneurysm of the cardiovascular apparatus. Patients with the suspicion of LDS should undergo an echocardiographic examination and genetic test. In patients with LDS and that already have a dilatation of the aortic root should undergo pharmacological therapy with a beta-blocker angiotensin II receptor inhibitor. Surgical treatment is indicated earlier than in patients with MFS (Tab. 10).

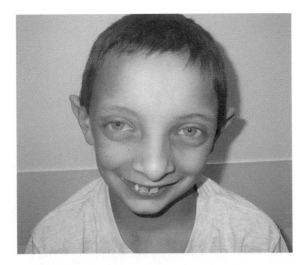

Fig. 48 _ Patient affected by LDS type 1, who has the characteristic craniofascial features (Williams et al., 2007; Aalbetrs et al., 2008).

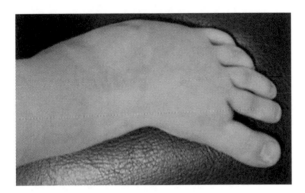

Fig. 49 _ Left lower limb of the patient seen in picture 48 (Aalberts et al, 2008).

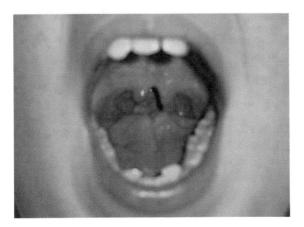

Fig. 50 _ Patient affected by LDS type 2 with bifid hypertrophic uvula (Aalberts et al, 2008).

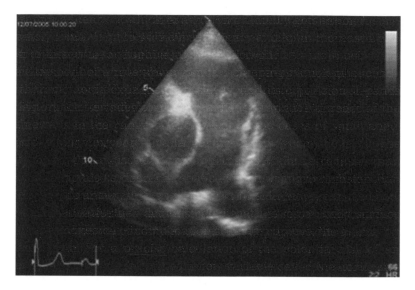

Fig. 51 _ Echocardiographic examination of a patient with significant anulo-aortic ectasis and a dilated pulmonary artery (Aalberts et al, 2008).

Indication criteria for cardiac surgery intervention in adult patients with LDS:
* diametre of the ascending aorta and/or aortic root ≥ 4.0cm or expansion ≥0.5cm/year,
* diametre of the descending aorta_>5.0cm or expansion _>0.5cm/year,
* diametre of the abdominal aorta_>5.0cm or expansion _>0.5cm/year,
* rapid progression in any segment of the aorta or a peripheral aneurysm.

Indication criteria for cardiac surgery intervention in children with LDS:
* craniofascial features of LDS,
    - craniofascial features: z-score of the aortic root >3.0cm or expansion ≥0.5cm/year,
    - moderate craniofascial features: z-score of the aortic root >4.0cm or expansion ≥0.5cm/year,
* a cardiac surgical intervention should be indicated later, respectively and at the diametre of the aortic annulus ≥ 1.8cm in order to permit a reconstruction procedure on the aortic root and valve with a big enough vascular prosthesis with the emphasis on the child growth,
* craniofascial features: z-score of the aortic root >3.0cm or expansion ≥0.5cm/year
* large aneurysm or significant dynamic progression in the descending segment of the aorta or large peripheral aneurysm (Aalberts et al, 2008).

Tab. 10. _ Indications criteria for surgical treatment of LDS (Aalberts et al, 2008).

3.3.2.3 Turner syndrome

Turner syndrome (TS) is one of the most frequent genetic disorders that affects only females with an incidence in 1:2000 to 1:2500 births. It is a genetic conditioned disease which affects girls and its cause is the partial or the total loss of the female chromosome X (monosomia X, caryotype 45, X). It happensduring the intrauterine development and the exact cause is not known. Women with TS have typical characteristic features – they are short (small BSA in m²), they have frequent pigment spots, skin wrinkle in the canthus of the eye (epicanthus), double or a horeshoe kidney, short neck, and other features (Fig. 52). In 50% of the cases the patients have congenital heart defects, most frequent is the bicuspid aortic valve and the aortic coarctation. The genetic cause is localised in the short segment (Xp) of the chromosome X (Price et al., 1983; Matura et al., 2007).

Congenital heart defects are the main cause of premature mortality of adult women with TS. Dissection of the aorta affects patients with TS at

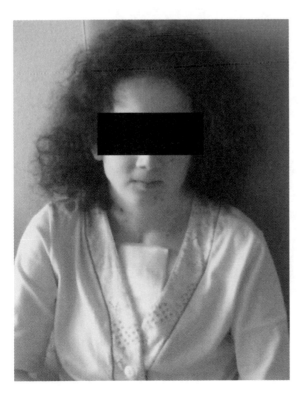

Fig. 52 _ Patient with typical features of TS (Sabol, 2013).

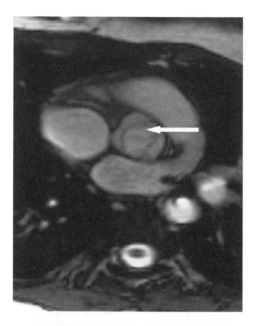

Fig. 53 _ MRI of the aortic valve, bicuspid aortic valve (arrow) in a patient with TS (Klaskova et al., 2010).

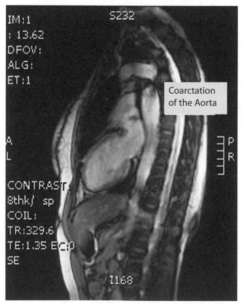

Picture 54 _ MRI of the thoracic aorta in a female patient with TS (Klaskova et al., 2010).

a lower age (average 36 years old). The aortic dissection is usually associated with risk factors, like the bicuspid aortic valve (Fig. 53), aortic coarctation (Fig. 54), aortic aneurysm, or arterial hypertension. The risk of rupture or aortic dissection during pregnancy is more than 2% and the risk of death in a pregnant patient with proved TS is 100 times higher. For this reason in 2006, the Practice Committee of the American Society of Reproductive Medicine published recommendations to perform detailed screening cardiologic examinations including echocardiographic examination and magnetic resonance imaging of the heart and great vessels in all women with a confirmed TS that plan a pregnancy. In women with any risk factors of aortic dissection the pregnancy is contraindicated (Klaskova et al., 2010).

Imaging with a MRI proved that 50% of the cases of the patients affected by Turner syndrome have an elongated aortic arch and a significant angle of the distal part of the aortic arch at the site of the Botallo duct. This state is called a pseudostenosis of the aortic isthmus and it is frequently associated with a poststenotic (postcoarctation) dilatation or aneurysm of the descending aorta. Other vascular abnormalities include pulmonary anomalous venous return, persistent left vena cava superior (in 13% of the patients), defect of the interatrial septa, and prolapse of the mitral valve.

On the basis of the combination of the echocardiography and the CTA examination it was proved that up to 75% of patients affected by TS have a cardiovascular abnormality. Similar to MFS the dissection of the ascending aorta occurs earlier than its dilatation (Matura et al., 2007).

The only scientific publication that addressed the epidemiology of the aortic dilatation in women with TS comes from the Danish archive. It was found that in women with TS the aortic dilatation occurred in 78 patients/100000 residents/year versus less than 1 woman /100000 residents/year in the non-affected part of the female Danish population within the ages of 30-40 years old. The average age of patients with TS with dilatation of the aorta was 35 years old and 25% of them did not have any predisposing factors for the development of the aortic dissection except the diagnosis of TS. The bicuspid aortic valve and the arterial hypertension were risk factors in the same rate in females without TS. The increase incidence of the aortic dilatation in patients with TS was confirmed also in other scientific studies (Karnis et al.,2003 ; Matura et al., 2007).

The indications for cardiac surgical intervention take into account the aortic size index (ASI, diametre of the ascending aorta relative to the size surface of the person, see chapter 3.2). In ASI >2cm/m^2 in individuals with TS needed more frequent controls of the cardiovascular apparatus (mainly aorta) in shorter intervals. In the value ASI $\geq$ 2.5 cm/m^2 we already discussed the significant dilatation that is associated with a high risk of rupture or dissection of the aorta. In patients with such values of ASI or with an absolute diametre of the ascending aorta 4.5 cm require preventive cardiac surgical intervention.

In the pharmacological treatment once again most important are beta-blockers and the angiotensin II receptors antagonists. If the primary capture of the aortic dilatation was on the basis of echocardiography, it is recommended a more detailed examination with a MRI or CTA.

3.3.2.4 Alagille syndrome

Alagille syndrome (AGS) is a dominant form of hereditary multisystem disorder that includes diseases of the liver, heart, eyes, face, skeleton, and other systems. This disorder is caused by a mutation of the gene JAG 1 which is found on 20th chromosome that plays a role in the signalisation between neighbour cells during the embryonal development. Mutations in

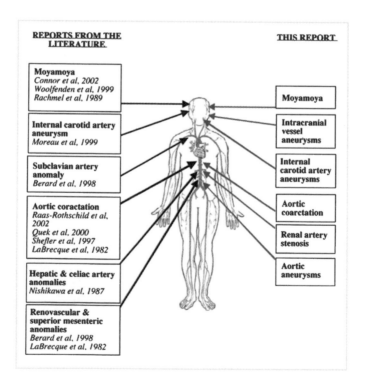

Fig. 55 _ Spectrum and localisation of the vascular complications in the group of patients with AGS (Kamath et al., 2004).

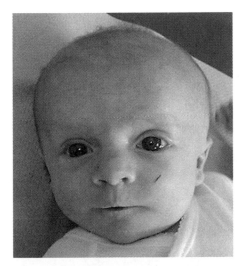

Fig. 56 _ Typical facial features-broad forehead, deep sunken eyes, and pointed chin (LeGloan et al., 2008).

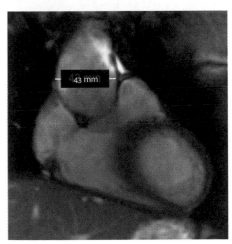

Fig. 57 _ MRI (sagital cut) of an aneurysm of the ascending aorta and aortic root in a child with AGS (Molinero-Herguedas et al., 2008).

JAG 1 disturb the signalisation process (path) which cause failures in development, mainly of the heart, the intrahepatic biliary track, the spine, in the vascular system, and in some facial features. The main signs of AGS are cholestasis, congenital heart defects, mainly the stenosis of the pulmonary valve, disorders in the development of the vertebrae (unusual shape of a butterfly), and some eye malformations. A lot of people with AGS have similar facial features including a broad forehead, deep sunken eyes, and a pointed chin (Fig. 56). The localisation and the extent of the vascular complications are captured in Figure 55 (Kamath et al., 2004).

A disorder in the development of the pulmonary artery or its valve that can cause different degrees of stenosis is considered the characteristic abnormality of AGS. According to the publication by Kamath et al. a stenosis of the pulmonary branches was found in up to 83% of the cases of the patients with AGS. Also observed were aneurysms of the ascending aorta at the sinuses of Valsalva, therefore the aortic root (Fig. 57). The vascular complications are responsible for 34% death of the patients with AGS. They have a dynamic character and can exist in every age. According to current facts, persons with AGS must have a thoroughly examined vascular system, mainly if they begin to manifest symptoms, for example neurologic deficiency, constant headaches, high blood pressure, and other (Kamath et al., 2004).

3.3.2.5 Bicuspid aortic valve

If we do not count the bicuspid aortic valve (BAV), then all congenital heart defects are found in approximately 0.8% of live births. Considering that the BAV by itself is 1-2% and that approximately in 1/3 of the cases tend to develop severe complications, then the bicuspid aortic valve by itself causes higher mortality and morbidity than all the rest of the congenital heart defects (Yankah, 2010).

The congenital malformation of the aortic valve instead of three leaflet two are developed, so called bicuspid valve, occurs twice more frequently in men than in women. This estimation may be to some extent inaccurate, because it is based on autopsy studies. The echocardiographic diagnosis has been available mainly in the last decade of the last century, while are in disposition only some studies that explore the occurrence of the bicuspid aortic valve in the healthy population. In the families with BAV there is an autosomal dominant type of heredity with decreased penetration similar to cases of congenital aneurysms.

The echocardiographic examination may confuse the unicuspid valve as a bicuspid valve, and conversely a bicuspid valve with a partial fusion of the leaflets as a tricuspid valve. BAV can be found in association with other congenital heart defects, more frequently with the coarctation of the aorta, or an interrupted aortic arch.

The BAV is formed by two of nearly the same sized symmetric leaflets that are divided by two completely formed commissures and where two aortic sinuses are present. The valve thus is formed like a two leaflet; it is a true congenital malformation of the aortic valve-type 0,ap (Fig. 58). The

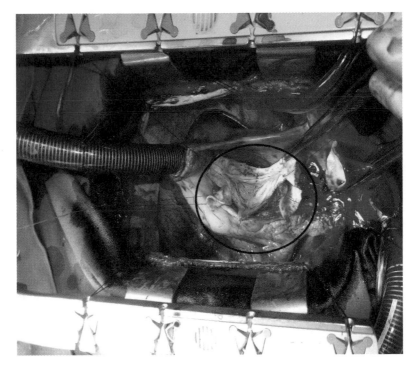

Fig. 58 _ Perioperative picture of BAV type 0ap (Kolesar, 2010)

most frequent variant is a condition where the leaflets of the bicuspid valve have different morphology. One of the leaflets has a preserved physiologic shape and the second is formed by a complete or incomplete fusion of two leaflets, which may happen during the prenatal or postnatal period. The size ratio of the two leaflets may be from 1:1 to 1:2, like in the case of fused two normally formed leaflets of the aortic valve. The size ratio of the two leaflets determines the angle between the two commissures. It vary in the range from 180° to 120° like it is in the tricuspid valve, and we call it –type 1 BAV. In the case of an incomplete growth the raphe is replaced by a cleft. The incidence of BAV with an incomplete fusion of the anterior leaflet is high, in operated patients groups, it is found in 70% of cases (Yankah, 2010).

The most frequent variant in more than 70% of cases is the fusion of the two coronary leaflets, which form the so-called anterior leaflet. The non-coronary leaflet is marked as a posterior leaflet. The second most common variant is the fusion of the right coronary leaflet with the non-coronary

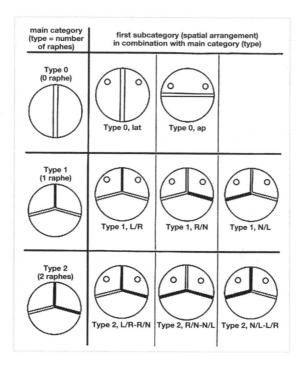

Fig. 59 _ Anatomic variants-phenotypes BAV (Yankah, 2010).

Type 0 (no raphae)
Type 1 (one raphae)
Type 2 (two raphae)

leaflet. The least frequent morphologic variant is the fusion of the left coronary and non-coronary leaflet. The anatomic variants-phenotypes of the bicuspid aortic valve are shown in Figure 59.

We divide the BAV on the basis of three parameters: number of raphae, localisation of raphae, and the relationship of the raphae to the origin of the coronary arteries. The function of the BAV can be normal until old age. The BAV manifests either as stenotic or regurgitant valve. The risk for the development of malfunction of the bicuspid valve is affected also by its phenotype. The development of the aortic stenosis or regurgitation is more frequent at the fusion of the right coronary and non-coronary leaflet. A true aortic regurgitation occurs approximately in 15-20% of patients with a bicuspid aortic valve and the disease is manifested most often in young or middle-aged patients. At the insufficiency of the bicuspid valve, when the regurgitation is caused by the excess tissue of the fused leaflet, only rarely leads to the development of stenosis. This reality presents a significant potential for the implementation of repair of these valves. The disease can manifest in any age, more often though in young patients. Bicuspid valve is more prone to develop an infective endocarditis (Yankah, 2010, Vojacek, 2009).

The coincidence of the bicuspid valve with the dilatation of the ascending aorta is well known and is found in 50-80% of individuals with this malformation. The affection of the ascending aorta is partially secondary, for example in the poststenotic dilatation of the aorta in the long term aortic regurgitation. Given that the dilalation of the aorta is often connected with a physiological functional bicuspid valve, it is rather a congenital disease of the vascular wall, like in Marfan syndrome. In the BAV are significantly thinner elastic lamella (lamina elastic interna et externa) of the aortic media and also the distance between them is more than in the aortic wall at the tricuspid valve. The total diametre of the aortic media is not in this malformation significantly thinner. The width of the elastic lamellae is inversely proportional of the diametre (dilatation) of the ascending aorta, on the other hand, the distance of the lamina interna and externa of the aortic media is proportional to the diametre (dilatation) of the ascending aorta (Yankah, 2010).

In patients with BAV, the changes on the vascular wall of the proximal aorta are connected with a decrease concentration of fibrillin-1. The coarctation of the aorta at the predilection site with the presence of BAV (up to 50% of these patients have BAV) shows that the abnormal tissue of the aorta reach until the distal aortic arch and the proximal descending aorta. The rate of progression of the diametre of the aortic aneurysm in patients with a BAV is 0.19cm/year versus 0.13cm/year in patients with a tricuspid aortic valve (TAV). Patients with BAV that are affected by a stenosis of the aortic valve, have a higher rate of progression (0.20cm/year) than patients with an insufficient BAV (0.14cm/year) (Nisri et al., 1999, Davies et al., 2007).

The above mentioned coincidence of BAV with a dilation of the ascending aorta can be explained on the basis of two probable mechanisms:

- increased hemodynamic load in the proximal part of the aorty that can lead to the gradual dilatation of the aorta (asymmetric flow and turbulence in the bicuspid valve);
- genetic abnormality of the structure of the aortic root;

The basis of these findings may seem that in BAV the aorta is dilated on the background of a genetic defect of the aortic wall and as a result of an abnormal hemodynamic stress on the aortic wall. The dilatation of the aorta is found in two basic phenotypes.

- affection of the whole ascending aorta, including the aortic root;
- isolated dilatation limited on the ascending aorta above the sinotubular junction (Fig. 60).

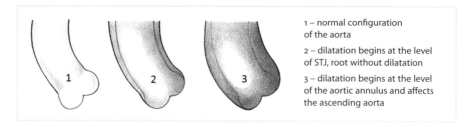

1 – normal configuration of the aorta

2 – dilatation begins at the level of STJ, root without dilatation

3 – dilatation begins at the level of the aortic annulus and affects the ascending aorta

Fig. 60 _ Animation of the phenotypes of the dilatation of the ascending aorta (Valocik, 2013, modified according Prof. Zacek, Hradec Kralove, CR).

The second type, which is the isolated dilatation of the aorta above the sinotubular junction is the most frequent and is found in up to 80% of the cases (Dominik, 2008). The stenosis of the aortic wall is a risk factor for the dilatation of the aorta above the sinotubular junction; aortic regurgitation is a risk factor for the dilatation of the aortic root. The affection of the aortic root is usually less frequent, more often, it is found in young patients with aortic regurgitation. Compared with the normal population, patients with a bicuspid aortic valve have an increased risk of dissection of approximately nine times. The dissection of the aorta is caused in 5% of cases with this type of malformation. In Marfan syndrome, this risk is significant higher, in approximately in 40% of cases. Therefore in the comparison of incidence in both diseases (1-2% against 0.01%) it is clear that the bicuspid valve is a more frequent cause for aortic dissection than Marfan syndrome (Vojacek, 2009).

Another relatively rare congenital defect of the aortic valve is the unicuspid aortic valve. Its incidence in the larger echocardiographic groups of adult population presents 1.02%. The presence of the unicuspid aortic valve is similar to the case of bicuspid valve often connected with a dilatation of the ascending aorta (48%). The unicuspid aortic valve most often has a surgical solution up to the age of 40 years old, where a reconstructive procedure if technically possible is preferred to the implantation of a valve replacement. The main criteria for the echocardiographic confirmation of the diagnosis of the unicuspid (unicommissural) valve is the existence of only one functional commissure. The other two commissures are rudimentary, which means that (in the horizontal axis) in the aortic wall are attached below the origin of the coronary vessels. The most frequent functional commissure is the commissure between the left coronary and non-coronary leaflet (Schäfers, 2008; Yankah, 2010).

Yasuda et al., found that the isolated replacement of the BAV does not avoid the dilatation of the aorta later in time. All patients with a stenotic aortic valve had increased progression of the dilatation of the aorta called poststenotic dilatation of the aorta. Likely as a result of increased pressure below the stenotic BAV. In the case of the aortic insufficiency the dilatation of the aorta seen on the proximal part of the ascending aorta is unlike the aortic stenosis (AS) in which the distention is seen more distally. It seems that the dilatation on the proximal part of the ascending aorta and/or root has is a result of the failure of the valve or proceeds the same time with the failure. In the stenotic BAV the changes in the hemodynamic parameters (flow) have as a result the faster dilatation of the aorta, thus there is a higher risk/rupture in BAV with valve stenosis (Yasuda, 2003).

On the basis of the ACC/AHA (American) guidelines and ECS (European) cardiology society from 2012 in connection with the diagnosis and treatment of the patients affected with a disease of the thoracic aorta at the BAV we dictate surgical replacement of the aneurysmal ascending aorta in cases where the diametre is more than 5.0cm (in the ESC guidelines from 2010 the borderline figure was 4.5 cm) (Erbel et al, 2014).

According to Svensson, the preventive replacement of the ascending aorta is directed if the aortic diametre is more than 4.5 cm (like the previous ESC guidelines in 2010) if the ratio of the aortic aneurysm area to the height of the patient is more than $8cm^2/m^2$. Also, we recommend that a surgical intervention is not needed on the valve (BAV) to replace the ascending aorta in patients with the ratio of the aortic aneurysm area to the height of the patient is more than $10cm^2/m^2$. Similar recommendations are presented by Etz on which patients with a good function of the bicuspid aortic valve a replacement of the ascending aorta is performed if its diametre is more than 5.0cm (identical with the guidelines ESC in 2012) (Etz et al., 2010). Findings from the scientific study by Park and authors suggest that if the aortic arch is connected with the BAV do not fulfil classic criteria for its replacement during the time of the replacement of the ascending aorta, it is unlikely that in the future would dilate in this condition that would be needed another cardiac reoperation (Park et al., 2011).

3.3.2.6 Ehlers-Danlos syndrome

Ehlers-Danlos syndrome (EDS) is a group of congenital disorders that affect the connective tissue – mainly the skin, articulations, and the vascular wall. The incidence of EDS is rare. In patients with EDS abnormalities in the connective tissue appear, specifically in the synthesis and the metabolism of the collagen and other proteins of the connective tissue. This results in defective properties of the tissue, like the decreased elasticity, strength, and finally impaired wound healing. Among the dominant symptoms of EDS include the elastic and fragile skin and the hyperextensible articulation that exceed the normal range of movement (Fig. 61) (Steiner et al, 2009).

The first existence of the disease comes from Job van Mekeren in 1682. On the basis of a presentation in 1901 from Ehlers and in 1908 from Danlos, the name EDS was established (Hamano et al., 1994).

Particularly in the IV type of EDS (vascular type), the abnormal protein is collagen type III. This type of EDS is rare but the most severe. The heredity is autosomal dominant and the genetic abnormality appeared in the gene COL3AI that is found in the chromosomal region 2q31. The incidence of EDS is 1 in 5000-10000 residents. The average lifetime of patients with EDS is nearly normal, except in type IV, in which the average lifetime is 50 years old due to a rupture of arteries or the organs of the gastrointestinal tract. On the basis of clinical symptoms, we can divide EDS into ten types; however, they have common features. It is interesting that in half of the patients affected by EDS it is not possible on the basis of the clinical examinations to determine which type it is (Steiner et al., 2009). All the types of EDS have the following common features that manifest in different intensities:

- hyperelastic, velvety skin;
- hyperextensible articulations with many dislocations;
- fragile tissue;
- slow and insufficient wound healing (keloid wounds);
- significant trend for the creation of subcutaneous suffusions.

Mainly the fourth type of EDS is chacterised by transparent skin with freely seen subcutaneous veins. In this type of EDS the highest risk is the intestine rupture or any other abdominal organ, but mainly there is the risk of rupture of an artery that can lead to exsanguination and death. This is the main reason for the average life of 40-50 years old for these types of patients. Except these potential serious complications, patients with EDS have a common facial appearance with prominent eyes, thin lips and nose, and a sunken face with a small chin.

The arterial aneurysm in children with EDS usually affect the aorta, on the other hand in adults with EDS the affection of the arterial system is multiple and includes the aorta as well as the peripheral arteries (Hetzer et al., 2008).

Fig. 61 _ The hyperxtension of the fingers is easy and without pain (Steiner et al., 2009).

3.3.2.7 Sphrintzen-Goldberg syndrome

It is a rare genetic abnormality with a marfanoid phenotype that is characterised by craniosynostosis and significant craniofascial features, neurologic affection with an intermediate severe mental disorder and also cardiovascular abnormalities. It appears rarely and they are observed mutations of the gene that codes fibrilin-1. Histological samples from people with Sphrintzen-Goldberg syndrome (SGS) and an aortic dissection show cystic medionecrosis. The form of heredity is not known (Lee et al., 2000).

The clinical diagnosis is based on the combination of the following main symptoms (Greally et al., 1998):

- craniofascial features: craniosynostosis, exophalmus, hypertelorismus, maxilar hypoplasis, micrognathia, low-lying auricles;
- skeletal abnormalities: dolichostenomelia, arachnodactylia, pes planus, pectus excavatus, scoliosis, hypermobility, and contracture of the articulation (Fig. 62);
- brain and neurologic manifeststions: late motor and cognitive development, mild and intermediate intellectual disorder, hydrocephalus, dilatation of the lateral ventricles;

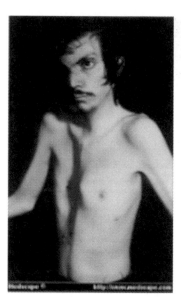

Fig. 62 _ Facial and thorax deformity (Lee et al., 2000).

- pneumothorax, abdominal hernia;
- cardiovascular symptoms (at the most severe forms of the SGS): mitral valve prolapse with mitral regugurgitation, regurgitation of the aortic valve, occasionally aneurysm of the aorta (case reports).

Many patients with a "marfan-like" phenotype with characteristic deformities, like the Lujan-Fryns syndrome, congenital spastic arachnodactylia (CCA) and other can be manifested with severe cardiovascular symptoms (aneurysm, aortic dissection), for that it is recommended frequent and thorough cardiovascular preventive controls.

3.3.2.8 Osteogenesis imperfecta

Osteogenesis imperfecta (OI) is a heterogenic disorder of the synthesis of the connective tissue with a dominant form of heredity. This is caused by a defect in the synthesis of the collagen type I. Sometimes it is known as the disease of the fragile bones. Patients affected by this genetic disorder have a very fragile skeleton, and as a result of it they often have fractures. This is one of the basic characteristics of the disease. Other tissues rich of collagen are also affected.. The initial manifestation and the intensity of the symptoms show a strictly individual diversity (Radunovic et al., 2011).

Four clinical types of this disorder were indentified based on clinical, radiological, and genetic studies:

- type I: includes patients with mild symptoms;
- type II: is severe and usually lethal in the perinatal period;
- type III: patients with severe symptoms;
- type IV: patients with mild and intermediate severe symptoms.

Recently another four types of this disease were indentified. Type V has similar clinical symptoms to type IV, but it has uniquely histology findings. Also type VI has similar clinical manifestations to type IV, but it has a specific histology finding. Patients with type VII show an abnormal composition of the cartilage and patients with type VIII appeared with a pathologic composition of the protein leprecan.

The collagen type I forms 75% of the total collagen, that is found in the heart myocardium and also participates in the composition of the aortic wall. A scientific study by Radunovic showed that patients with OI have

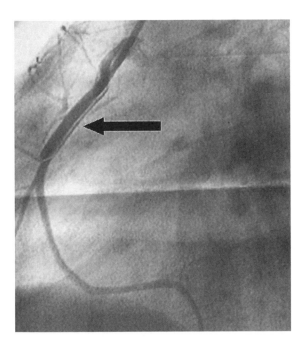

Fig. 63 _ Dissection of the right coronary artery in a patient with osteogenesis imperfecta. The dissection involves the whole proximal segment of the artery (arrow) (Escola et al., 2002).

a larger dimension and weight of the left heart ventricle than the control samples of healthy individuals. At the same time a higher incidence of the arterial hypertension in the group affected by this disease was found. Patients with type III had more severe pathologic findings than the group of patients with OI type I and IV. Many authors believe that the higher parametres of the left heart ventricle are not only the result of the arterial hypertension but as well as from its own disease.

In the group of patients with OI, it was observed a more frequent incidence of failure of the aortic and mitral valve. The diametre of the aorta in the patients with OI relative to the BSA was larger than the diametre of the aorta relative to the BSA in individuals in the control sample. Patients with type III had a more significant dilatation of the abdominal aorta than patients with type I and IV (Radunovic et al., 2011).

Occasionally case reports confirmed that the incidence of aneurysms and dissections in OI is possible in the whole arterial system. In Figure 63 it shows a dissection of the right coronary artery (Escola et al., 2002).

Aneurysms in the part of the abdominal aorta and the intracranial aneurysms are the most often cardiovascular pathology which is found in patients with OI (Matouk et al., 2011). It is desirable that in patients with a diagnosed OI type III, to perform more frequent controls due to the possible occurrence of cardiovascular complications.

3.3.2.9 Beals syndrome – CCA (Congenital Contractural Arachnodactyly)

Beal's syndrome or Congenital Contractural Arachnodactyly (CCA) is a genetic disease with an autosomal dominant type of heredity. It manifests with identical skeletal abnormalities like in the case of MFS, with the difference being that the ophthalmological symptoms are characteristic in Marfan syndrome and are rarely found in CCA. The cause of the mentioned syndrome is a mutation of the gene FBN2, which is in the chromosome located very near to the gene FBN1 (this is affected by a mutation in Marfan syndrome).

The clinical symptoms include contractures of the articulations (progressive deterioration of the extension) and an abnormal shape of the auricle. From the cardiovascular features dominates the aortic dilatation to aneurysm (National Marfan Foundation http://www.marfan.org/marfan/2347/Beals-Syndrome/CCA). In Mexico, it was described that within one family there were three members that suffered from this disease. During the last five years, repeated echocardiographic examinations that were done on the affected children found a progressive dilatation of the aortic root, but without a dissection of the aortic wall. In contrast, the mother who is also affected by this disease had during the whole period of examination physiological findings on the aortic root (Gupta et al., 2002, 2004).

We propose that patients suffering from this disease should be evaluated for any possible presence of a disease of the thoracic aorta and should be tested for the incidence of any cardiovascular complications.

3.3.2.10 Autosomal dominant polycystic kidney disease

Autosomal dominant polycystic kidney disease (PKD) is a disease that is conditioned by many genetic defects mostly localised on the 16 chromosome. Usually presents as asymptomatic, which is why less than 50% of the cases are diagnosed. For the determination of the diagnosis the medical history, ultrasound examination of the kidneys and genetic examination are substantial. The disease can be complicated with the manifestation of the cardiovascular symptoms, like aneurysms in the arterial system of the CNS, dilatation of the thoracic aorta or heart valve disease.

The relationship between the abdominal aorta and the dilatation of the thoracic aorta with PDK is not clearly defined. The literature describes few of these cases; there are mainly patients who are affected by this disease and at the same time they do not fulfill the diagnostic criteria for Marfan syndrome. In autopsy samples of these patients there was the presence of the aneurysm of the thoracic aorta seven times higher than in the normal population. Arterial hypertension is one of the most important predisposing factors that contributes to the pathophysiology of the dilatation of the thoracic aorta. At the present time, there do not exist relevant information, that reveals the number of the regular controls of the thoracic aorta with the help of the different imaging methods (Toluola et al., 2001).

3.3.2.11 Noonan syndrome

Noonan' syndrome (NS) is a relative frequent autosomal dominant congenital disorder, which is considered as a type of dwarfism that affects men as well as women. The genetic disorder includes an alteration of four genes – PTPN11, SOS1, RAF1, and KRAS. The incidence of the disease is 1 in 1000 to 1 in 2500. Characteristic symptoms of the syndrome are:

a) congenital heart defects (stenosis of the pulmonary valve, hypertrophic cardiomyopathy, aneurysm of the aortic root and other);
b) short growth (dwarfism);
c) hemostasis disorders, aesy creation of suffusions;
d) special facial features – flat nose, hypertelorismus, oblique eyes slots, and eyelids ptosis.

Patients affected by this syndrome were sporadically diagnosed with large aneurysms of the aortic root at the site of the sinuses of Valsalva. From the last series of 129 patients, 52% had an aneurysm of the aortic root originated from the right coronary sinus, in 34% of patients from the non-coronary sinus, and in 12% of cases the maximal changes localised in the left coronary sinus were found (Purnel et al., 2005). The nature of the majority of the aneurysms has a basis in the congenital inferiority (medionecrosis) of the aortic wall. The aneurysm in NS in the majority of patients have no clinical symptomatology and also rarely a rupture or aortic dissection happens. However, if the aneurysm of the aortic root is significant, it can be manifested as an insufficiency of the aortic valve, obstruction of the outflow tract of the right heart ventricle, pressure on the coronary arteries, atrioventricular block of the III degree, and finally it can be the affected wall of the aortic root a source of embolisation to the system of the CNS (Purnel et al., 2005).

3.3.2.12 Klippel-Feil syndrome

The Klippel-Feil syndrome (KFS) was first described by the neurologists Maurice Klippel and Anre Feil. The incidence of this disease is the context of inheritance sporadic, in the literature it is stated that the autosomal dominant as well as the recessive form. The etiology is multifactorial with an incidence of 1 in 42000 newborns. It is interesting that on the basis of autopsy samples it seems likely that the family line of pharao Tutanchamon suffered from this disease (Kawano et al., 2006; Khawaya et al., 2009; Zaki et al., 2010; Sullivan et al., 2012).

We talk about a segmental disorder of the development of the cervical vertebrae combined with different organs abnormalitie.. The main features of the disease are:

- musculoskeletal disorders;
- genitourinary disorders;

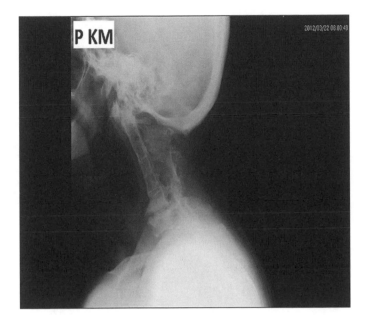

Fig. 64 _ Sciagraphic examination of the cervical spine in a patient with KFS. Synostosis in the typical site of the cervical spine (Sabol et al., 2014).

- abnormalities of the senses;
- cardiovascular malformations (in 4-5%).

The diagnosis of the disease is based on the classic triad musculoskeletal symptoms which are:

a) synostosis of the cervical vertebrae (Fig. 64);
b) low hair line;
c) significant limited cervical mobility.

The cardiovascular disorders for this disease are affiliated only in 4% to 5% of the cases. Most frequently the following occur: the coarctation of the aorta (Sabol et al., 2014), postcoarctation pseudoaneurysm (Fig. 65, 66), regurgitation of the mitral valve, or defect of the interventricular septum (Albright, 2007).

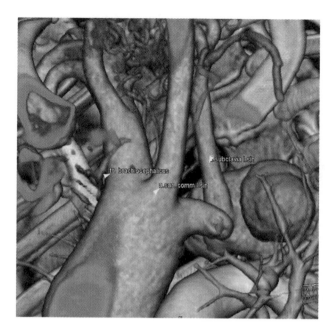

Fig. 65 _ Preoperative CTA reconstruction of a patient with KFS and cardio-vascular abnormalities: hypoplastic distal aortic arch, coarctation of the aorta, postcoarctation aneurysm (Sabol, 2014).

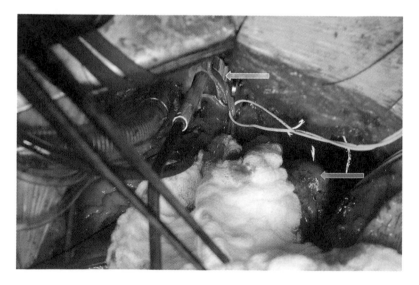

Fig. 66 _ Perioperative image of the open hypoplastic aortic arch in the distal part (white arrow), and a pseudoaneurysm (green arrow) distally from the coarctation in a patient with KFS (Sabol et al., 2014).

3.3.2.13 Pseudoxanthoma elasticum

Pseudoxanthoma elasticum (PXE), also known under the name of Gron-blade-Strandberg syndrome, is a genetic disease caused by the fragmentation and mineralisation of the elastic fibers in some tissue. Most frequently skin and eye symptoms occur, in the later period, it attacks the arterial system, mainly from the cause of premature atherosclerosis. It is caused by an aotosomal recessive mutation of the gene ABCC6 in the short arm of the chromosome 16 (16p). Women are twice as affected than men. The most common age of the manifestation of the disease is at the age of 13 (Chassaing et al., 2005).

The clinical symptomatology is manifested mainly on the skin, with yellow prominent papular lesions in the cervical region (Fig. 67), in the axilla, in the groin or in the inner sites of the knee and elbow joint. From the eye signs there is an affection of the retina that is visualised in an ophtalmological examination. We call this "peau d' orange" which roughly means, that the retina is similar to orange coloration. Mineralisation in the retina causes the creation of retinal hemorrhage, that can lead to the disorder of the cental vision (Chassaing et al., 2005).

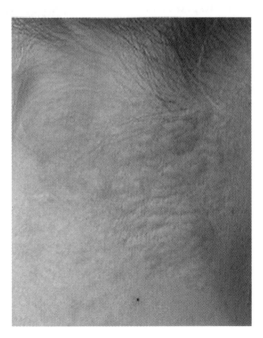

Fig. 67 _ Pseudoxanthoma elsticum of the back site of the neck: yellowish soft prominent humps (characteristic sign) (Wikipedia-free).

Except from these skin and eye symptoms the disease is chacterised by the affection of the gastrointestinal (stomach bleeding) and cardiovascular tract. The cardiovascular complications include the ischemic disease of the lower limbs and the heart and rarely also an aneurysm of the ascending aorta (Farmakis et al., 2004).

3.3.2.14 Klinefelter syndrome

Klinefelter syndrome (KS) is a disease that affects men, it is characterised by the existence of one or two extra X chromosomes and it is the most frequent genetic etiology for primary sterility. The most frequent is the form one X chromosome more (47,XXY). The prevalence of the disease is around 1 in 660 newborn boys. In the patients with KS, there is a higher occurrence of breast cancer (Aksglaede et al., 2013).

The clinical symptoms mainly concern the reproductive system, the habit (tall growth), musculoskeletal apparatus, and sporadically the cardiovascular system mainly aneurysms of the abdominal aorta (Umscheid et al., 2007).

3.3.3 Aneurysm with a non-infectious inflammatory etiology

Systematic inflammatory diseases can cause also an aortitis and an inferiority of the aortic wall which result can be an aortic aneurysm and in the cases of affection of the aortic root also an insufficiency of the aortic valve.

Among these diseases are:

1. Giant cell arteritis – Horton's disease;
2. Takayasu arteritis;
3. Behcet disease;
4. Wiskott-Aldrich syndrome;
5. Collagen diseases (systemic lupus-SLE and ankylosing spondylitis –SA, Bechterew disease);
6. IBD (Inflammatory Bowel Disease) – ulcerative colitis;
7. Cogan syndrome;
8. Prolapsing polychondritis;
9. Reiter syndrome (reactive arthritis);
10. Churg-Strauss syndrome (granulomatous vasculitis);
11. Sarcoidosis;

12. Idiopathic isolated aortitis;
13. Ormond's disease (Idiopathic Retroperitoneal Fibrosis).

Chowdhary et al. researched the predisposing risk factors that are associated with an aortitis of the ascending aorta. The study states the finding of two factors. Which are being female and smoking (Chowdhary et a., 2009):

a) The disease is observed in women after menopause caused by the effect of sexual hormones. These hormones affect the integrity of the aortic wall and regulate the production and function of the elastin/collagen. The beta-estradiol increases the ratio of elastin/collagen in favour of the elastin that results in the increased elasticity of the aorta. According to the research, this results in the role of the hormones in the mutual interaction of immunologic and proteolytic systems in the regulation of inflammation in the rigid and inflexible aorta.
b) Smoking has a significant role in the development of atherosclerosis, which increasse the degradation of the elastin as an inflammatory answer of the organism. It affects the proteolytic enzymes, for example, MMPs, elastase, cystein-protease and lipoxygenase, which have a destructive role in the intercellular matrix and so they increase the risk for the development of an aneurysm. An increase in MMP-1, MMP-2, MMP-8 and MMP-9 in the endothelial cells was observed. At the same time, smoking enters into complicated gene and immune mechanisms, for example HLA (human leukocyte antigen) system and more, which increase and accelerates the creation of vasculitis in predisposed individuals.

3.3.3.1 Giant cell arteritis

Giant cell arteritis (GCA; Horton's disease-temporal arteritis) is a disease caused by the immune system with characteristic granulomatous infiltrations on the wall of intermediate large and large arteries. It is the most frequent primary vasculitis. In the general population, it occurs with a frequency of 13 to 25 times in 100000 residents, where the higher frequency of occurrence is in Scandinavian countries and in North America. Being females and over the age of 50 years old are risk factors. The incidence rate is increasing with age. It affects only large and intermediate large arteries. In the past it prevailed that the affected artery was only the temporal artery or other arteries supplying the CNS. Later it was shown that also the aorta (including primary and secondary branches) can be affected with this disease. On the basis of the results of scientific studies, it was proved that patients with this disease have 17.3 times increased risk for the development of an aneurysm of the thoracic aorta (Fig. 68) (Zehr et a., 2005; Nuenninghoff et al., 2003; Gelsomino et al., 2005).

Also stenosis of the large arteries was observed, like the syndrome of the aortic arch, which is characterised by the lumen stenosis of the epiaortic vessels. This has results in claudication pain of the upper limbs in the case of stenosis of the subclavian artery, axillary artery, or brachial artery (Fig. 69). In the case of hemodynamic severe stenosis of the carotid arteries can lead to neurologic symptoms on the background of ischemia (transitory ischemic attack, stroke).

The syndrome of the aortic arch and the aneurysm of the ascending aorta are two different diseases that can both exist at the same time in one patient.

Granulomatous infiltrations occur also in individuals younger than 40 years old in the form of Takayasu arteritis (see 3.3.3.2.). As opposed to GCA, Takayasu arteritis affects the aorta and its branches significantly more frequently.

Vascular lesions in GCA are the result of the abnormal activation of the T-lymphocytes. There is a suspicion that the potential triggers are microor-

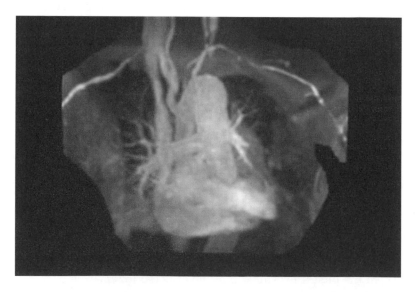

Fig. 68 _ MRI examination of a patient with a severe stenosis of Subclavian artery at the site of the pass to the Axillary artery (Nuenninghoff et al., 2003).

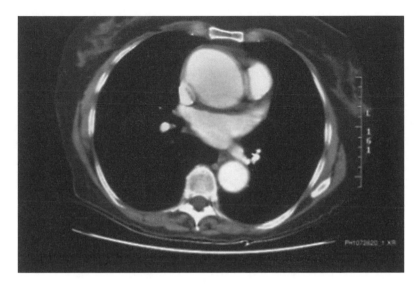

Fig. 69 _ CTA examination of the Ascending Aorta with Aneurysm in the background of GCA (Nuenninghoff et al., 2003).

ganisms (for example, mycoplasma or Chlamydia in pneumonia, parvovirus B19, parainfluenza virus and herpes viruses).

T – lymphocytes (CD4+) and activated macrophages (APC – antigen presenting cells) are mainly represented in inflammatory migration and infiltration of the aortic wall. Macrophages and lymphocytes penetrate to all the layers of the aortic wall and the primary immunologic destruction happens in the adventitia of the aorta. The main protagonist of this pathological immunological destruction is INF-γ (interferon gamma) that produce the T-cells. This subsequently activates the macrophages that cause the characteristic granulomatous reaction. The intensity of the activation of the T-lymphocytes with an excess production of INF-γ causes a significant intimal hyperplasia which lead to the organ ischemia.

If the T-lymphocytes produce an increased amount of interleukin 2 (IL-2) and a low amount of INF-γ, the vasculitis is developed without the obliteration of the arterial lumen. In the isolated rheumatic polymyalgia in the basis of histo-morphological criteria vasculitis is absent, but massive infiltration of T-lymphocytes and macrophages allows the detection of IL-2, IL-1, IL-6 in the tissue. The role of the macrophages is diverse. The macrophages that are found in the adventitia produce pro-inflammation entities that maximises the activation of the T-lymphocytes. These are found in the arterial media, around the leiomyocytes, are aimed for oxidation and production of MMPs, and take part in the destruction of the lamina elastica media (Fig. 70). Macrophages which are found in the border of media and intima produce the growth factors-PDGF (platelet-derived growth factor) and factors for neoangiogenesis –VEGF (vascular endothelial growth factor) (Fig. 71), which control the process of intimal hyperplasia. Reaction is the migration of the myofibroblasts to the subendothelial layer of the intima, as a consequence the excess mitosis and production of the extracellular matrix. This leads to the stenosis or total obliteration of the arterial lumen, which leads to the ischemia of the organ that is supplied by the affected artery. Concurrently with the vascular lesions in the organism it is observed an acute systemic inflammatory reaction. IL-6 has a significant role in the stimulation of the production of the acute phase proteins in the liver. The monocytes that are leached into the blood circulation, are the main source of IL-6. The mechanism and the site of activation of the monocytes and the macrophages in GCA and rheumatic polymyalgia are not yet known.

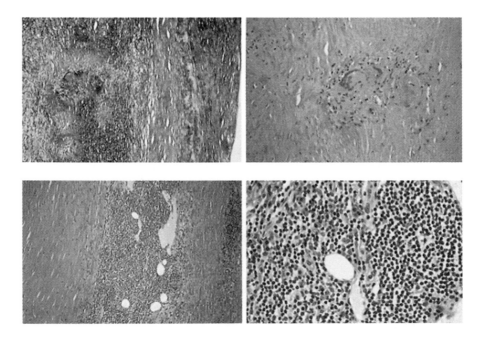

Picture 70 _ Destruction of the lamina elastica interna and media by large cells (hematoxyl-lin-eosin). The adventitia shows infiltration of mononuclears and chronic fibrosis (Nuenninghoff et al., 2003).

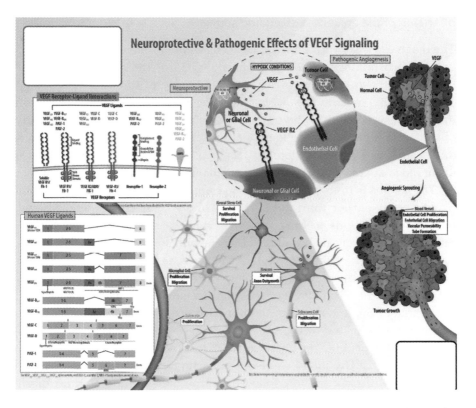

Fig. 71 _ Pathologic neoangiogenesis in hyperproduction of growth factors and factors for neoangiogenesis (PDGF, VEGF) (Nuenninghoff et al., 2003).

The extent of the clinical symptomatolgy is broad and includes symptoms that comes from the generalised systemic inflammatory disease (weakness, anorexia, weight loss, fever of unknown origin, night sweats, hyperpyrexia) and from the local complications according to the extent and the locality of the vascular affection.

a) Temporal arteritis

Affected are common carotid arteries, temporal arteries, occipital arteries, and spinal artery. Symptoms are: strong headaches, hypersensitivity of the sculp, weakness of the masseter and temporal muscles, ischemia of the tongue and part of the face, facial edema, dysphagia accompanied with pain. In the stenosis of an ophtalmica according to the severity of the stenosis can lead to galloping amaurosis, diplopia, and other complications.

b) Arteritis of the epiaortic vessels and aortitis

The diagnosis is set with imaging methods without the need for taking a biopsy. Approximately 50% of patients with GCA of the subclavian or axillary artery have a negative result of the biopsy of the temporal artery. The symptoms include the syndrome of the aortic arch with claudication intervals of weakness of the upper limbs, side asymmetry in the intensity of the pulse wave and systolic pressure of the upper limbs, hallucinations and in some cases even ischemic affection of the organs with necrosis. Also observed is an absence of cranial symptoms.

The aortitis is in 10-15% of cases is asymptomatic. The cranial symptoms usually occur earlier than the aortitis. Usually it affects the whole aorta, but the complications occur mostly in the thoracic aorta. The aortitis cause dilatation and even aneurysm of the aorta with subsequent complications, for example rupture or dissection of the aorta, at the affection of the aortic root also insufficiency of the aortic valve. It is not unusual to primary diagnose this disease from the perioperative aortic samples after excision of the wall of the aneurysm of the aorta, where it was not known that the patients were affected by GCA (Calvo-Romero et al., 2003).

The histomorphologic characteristic features are common with Takayasu arteritis. The initial stage of the aortitis is diagnosed with the help of CT and MRI examination, follow-up of the patients after the establishment of the diagnosis is necessary for many years.

c) Systemic inflammatory reaction and arteritis

In the clinical picture prevail the symptoms of the systemic inflammatory disease. The biopsy of the temporal artery is the diagnostic examination of the first choice and it should be performed even in the case of absence of sensitivity or palpable " nodules" in the artery.

d) Rheumatic polymyalgia

Approximately 50% of patients with GCS have rheumatic polymyalgia. This clinical syndrome is characterised by pain and muscle rigidity in the shoulder and pelvis.

Important findings for the diagnosis and indication for the surgical intervention of the aneurysm of patients with GCA was provided from the study by Zehr et al. from the Mayo Clinic USA. Thirty-seven patients with an aneurysm of the ascending aorta (Fig. 72, 73) underwent cardiac surgical procedure. The reason for the intervention was aneurysm of the ascending aorta with diametre > 5.5cm and symptomatic insufficiency of the aortic valve. In 8% of the cases, the diagnosis of GCA was confirmed on the basis of the biopsy. Twenty-seven percent of patients had in their medical history

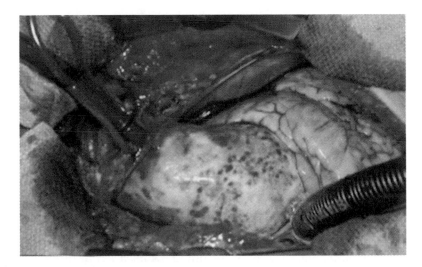

Fig. 72 _ Aneurysm of the ascending aorta with a diametre of 70mm in GCA (Zehr et al., 2005).

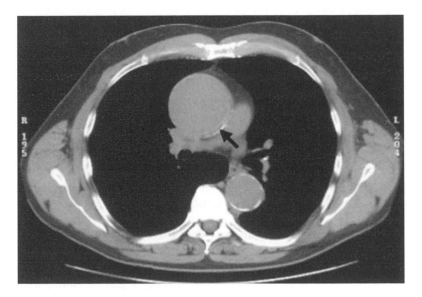

Fig. 73 _ CTA examination of an aneurysm of the ascending aorta in GCA. The arrow shows the site of thickening in the dorsal side of the aorta (Zehr et al., 2005).

had a temporal arteritis or rheumatic polymyalgia. The time interval from the moment of the establishment of the diagnosis to the cardiac surgical procedure was in the range of 8.9 ±3.4 years and the average diametre of the aneurysm was 6.1±0.8cm (Zehr et al., 2003).

The characteristic feature is the called the "paved" aorta with an intima that has a characteristic contour or picture of a "shelling" tree.

It is recommended that all patients who are affected by a temporal aortitis or for an arteritis of the great arteries are followed. The diseases of the aorta that are caused by GCA have a very high risk for severe complications such as a rapid progression on an aneurysm.

Also it is recommended that long term monitoring of the patients with the help of CTA examination, the diametre of the ascending aorta from which an operation is indicated is 5.5cm or less, if it is at the same time present also an insufficiency of the aortic valve.

Among the surgical procedures is the supracoronary replacement, in the case of an aneurysm of the aortic root then the Bentall operation or its alternatives:

- root remodeling (Yacoub) including stabilisation of the aortic annulus (implantation of an extra-aortic ring) for the reason for the prevention of late dilatation of the annulus (Lansac et al., 2009);
- aortic valve reimplantation (David I-V) (Cohn, 2011).

In case that the aneurysm reaches the aortic arch, we suggest a partial/total replacement of the arch. If it is aneurysmal and the descending aorta:

- two phase procedure – replacement of the aortic root (Bentall) / reconstruction of the root and ascending aorta and arch including elephant trunk in the first period and in the second period implantation of a stentgraft or surgical replacement from a thoracotomy;
- one phase procedure, replacement of the aortic root (Bentall) / reconstruction of the root and ascending aorta and arch including a stentgraft connected with a vascular prosthesis.

In the active phase of the disease it is recommended to treat with steroids. In patients whom the sedimentation (ESR) and C-reactive protein (CRP) are still elevated then cyclophophamid, azathioprin and dapson are added into the treatment. Currently it is not known whether it can be prevent the development of an aneurysm by the administration of high doses of steroids and antineoplastic medications.

In another scientific work by Gelsomino et al. in 10 patients with GCA, it was examined the natural development of these aneurysms. The reason for a surgical intervention were cardiac symptoms (dyspnea, fatique, weakness) in two patients, in another two it was heart failure and in the other six, it was the indication criterium the diametre of the aneurysm of the aorta. In eight patients, they was a diagnosed annuloaortic ectasia with the involvement or without the involvement of the aortic arch; in these patients an operation was performed according to Bentall and a replacement of the aortic arch if needed. In another two patients who did not have a dilated root, a supracoronary replacement of the ascending aorta and an isolated replacement of the aortic valve was performed. However during the post-operative follow-up these two patients had a dilatation and development of an aneurysm in the retained native part of the aorta (aortic root, sinuses of Valsalva). Even if it is a small group of patients and the results are not statistically important, the authors recommend for this reason in patients with GCA aortitis to perform a total replacement of the aortic root and ascending aorta regardless of the diametre before the operation. The authors also recommend in connection with the technical skills of the surgeon and experience of the cardiac surgery workplace instead the replacement of the aortic root and valve with a conduit (Bentall) to perform a reconstructive procedure on the aortic valve and aortic root (Yacoub, David), and nevertheless that the aortic leaflets showed definite signs of infiltration of mononuclear cells but without signs of granulomatous inflammatory process with the creation of large cells. Patients who during the postoperative period aplicated a steroid treatment, were asymptomatic and had physiologic levels of inflammatory parametres (Gelsomino et al., 2005).

3.3.3.2 Takayasu arteritis (syndrome of the aortic arch)

The Takayasu arteritis (TA) is an autoimmune disease that mainly affects the aorta and its main branches similarly the pulmonaty artery and its branches. It occurs globally in 2.6 of 100,000,000 residents. It affects predisposed young women (up to 80% of the cases) and middle-aged women, mainly women of Asian origin and particularly in the area of India. Only 15% of the patients with TA are older than 40 years old. The patients have an average life expectancy of 30 years (Ahmed et al., 2005).

This disease destroys the vascular wall, which can lead to the change of the lumen of the artery and thus to the stenosis up to the obliteration of the artery and to the development of an aneurysm and to peripheral embolisation. The pathophysiology of this disease is similar to GCA. Despite that its etiology is not known, it is characterised by a segmental and an irregular localised granulomatous inflammation of the aorta and its main branches. Most patients have systemic and local vascular symptoms, 20% of tpatients are asymptomatic and the diagnosis is only possible on the basis of pathological findings (autopsy samples). For the diagnosis of the disease mostly uses a CTA examination (Yamada et al., 1998).

For the diagnosis of TA, the American rheumatology society introduced diagnostic criteria, where for a positive diagnosis of TA at least three of the following symptoms must be present:

1. age 40 years old and less;
2. temporary weakness of the limbs;
3. decrease in the intensity of the pulse wave in one or both brachial arteries;
4. difference of 10mm Hg and more in the systolic pressure between the upper limbs;
5. murmur in one or both subclavia arteries or in the abdominal aorta;
6. stenosis or thrombosis of the aorta, its main branches or great vessels of the upper or lower limbs without atherosclerotic changes and without fibromuscular dysplasia of any other known etiology (Fig. 78, 79).

In the clinical symptomatology of the disease exists the following symptoms

*   general, non-specific (40% of the patients)
*   vascular (60-70% of the patients)
*   neurologic (60% of the patients)
*   respiratory and pulmonary (40%)
*   renal symptomatology (renovascular arterial hypertension)
*   skin
*   gastroenterologic
*   cardial (50% of the patients-insufficiency of the aortic valve, aneurysm of the aorta, dysrythmias, sudden death and so on)

Sueyoshi et al. examined in patients with TA the presence of the aortic aneurysms and its natural course. The aortic aneurysms occurred in 14 of 31 examined patients with TA (45%). The identification was performed on the basis of CTA examination. From the number of the patients, there were verified 17 aneurysms, three aneurysms on the ascending aorta (plus one on the same time on the descending aorta), three on the aortic arch (plus two on the same time on the descending aorta; Fig. 76, 77), one on the descending aorta (Fig. 74, 75), eight on the abdominal aorta. The average age of the patients was 42.1+-16.3 years old, where most of the patients of the group were women (12) (Sueyoshi et al., 2000).

From the study, some findings were found. The aortic aneurysm is formed on the aortic wall with minimal or no atherosclerotic involvement. During the acute phase of the disease, the induration of the aortic wall is

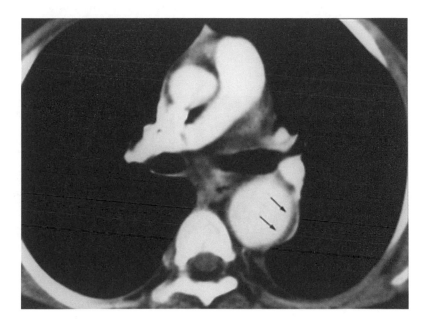

Fig. 74 _ CTA examination of a patient with an aneurysm of the descending aorta in TA. Arrows show the site with an active inflammatory process (Sueyoshi et al., 2000).

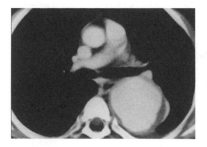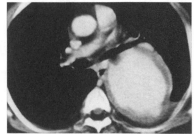

Fig. 75 _ CTA examination of the same patient (Fig. 74) with an aneurysm of the descending aorta in TA after two (left) and four (right) months; it is seen the evident progression of the disease (growth in the diametre of the aneurysm) and despite the early treatment with corticosteroids (Sueyoshi et al., 2000).

a characteristic sign in the CTA examination synchronously with the general signs of the generalised inflammatory process. These patients should be regularly controlled, because even the thickening of the aortic wall by itself does not mean an aneurismal change, it is proper to begin anti-inflammatory treatment with corticosteroids. From the 17 thoracic aneurysms, two recorded a significant progression of the diametre of the aorta with a rate 1,16cm/year with a subsequent rupture. In three cases the rate of growth of the aneurysm was 0.03cm/year without rupture. The authors also reported that the severity of the arterial hypertension is proportional to the rate of growth of the aortic aneurysm.

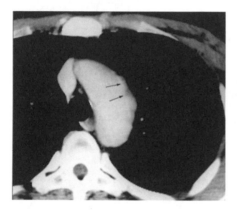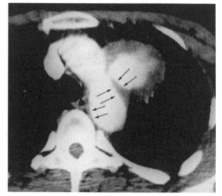

Fig. 76 _ CTA examination in a 45-years old female patient with an aneurysm of the arch and descending aorta in TA in the initial phase of the disease. The arrows show the inflammatory process with the thickening of the aortic wall (Sueyoshi et al., 2000).

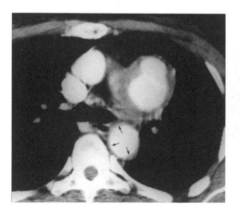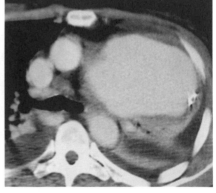

Fig. 77 _ CTA examination of the 45-years old same patient (fig. 76) with a progression of the aneurysm after 12 (left) and 15 (right) months (Sueyoshi et al., 2000).

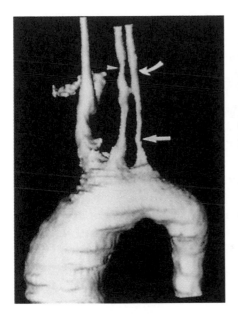
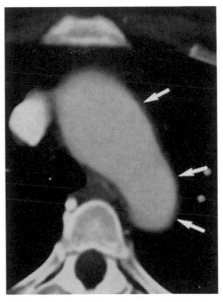

Fig. 78 _ CTA examination of a 17-years old patient with TA. Aneurysm of the ascending aorta and arch including stenosis of the epiaortic branches (Yamada et al., 1998).

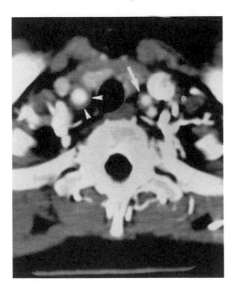
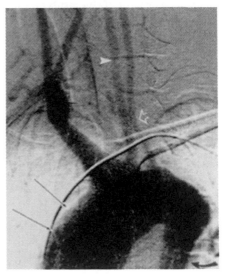

Fig. 79 _ CTA and aortography (right) examination of the same patient (picture 78) with TA.Left common carotid artery and subclavian artery are almost preobliterated (Yamada et al., 1998).

3.3.3.3 Behcet disease

Behcet's syndrome or Behcet disease (BS) is a systemic vasculitis of un-known origin, which is characterised by a repeated creation of ulcerative lesions in the mouth (aphthae) and in the region of the reproductive organs (ulcers). It affects eyes, joints, skin system, vascular, and the nervous system. It is named by the Turkish doctor Hulusi Behcet who described it in 1937. The disease can be manifested with complications, like the arteritis, however it is rare. The causes of BS are unknown; it is an idiopathic disease. Genetic predisposition can have some importance in the development of the disease. A definite factor that leads to the manifestation of BS is not known. If there are aneurysms, most are in the abdominal aorta, in the pulmonary or femo-ral artery. Aneurysms of the thoracic aorta are rarely found. An aneurysm of the coronary arteries is found more frequently, the manifestation of the disease in the form of coronary stenosis under the ischemic heart disease in BS is rare. The thrombosis of the coronary arteries is caused by the fibrous hyperplasia of the intima as a result of the vasculitis.

Bardakci et al. presented a case report of a 25-year-old patient affected by Behcet disease that was manifested under the picture of acute infarct of the anterior wall of the left heart ventricle with a 95% stenosis of the left an-terior descending artery and with hoarseness. The standard preoperative CTA examination surprisingly showed a saccular aneurysm of the aortic

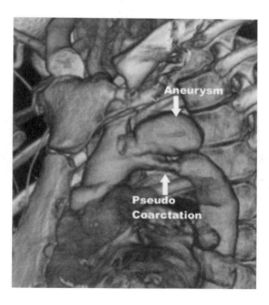

Fig. 80 _ CTA examina-tion showing a saccular aneurysm and pseudo-coarctation of the aortic arch (Bardakci et al., 2007).

arch (Fig. 80) that compromised the left subclavian artery and subsequently the remaining part of the arch (Bardakci et al., 2007).

For the revascularisation of the left anterior descending artery the authors used a graft from the great saphenous vein. Guidelines for the surgical revascularisation of the myocardium however clearly recommend (class I, level of evidence A) using an arterial graft from the left internal thoracic artery however, given the risk of the stenosis of the left subclavian artery it was not used. The question remains why this arterial graft was not used as a free graft or why was a graft not used from the right thoracic internal artery.

In the case of a saccular aneurysm of the arch of the aorta was after its partial excision used dacron patch (Fig. 81). With this the whole part of the affected aorta (arch) was not removed. We think that the interposition of a tubular prosthesis, although it is time consuming, is a preferable choice in view of the patient's age.

Patients with BS require a systematic treatment with corticosteroids and the vascular system should be examined. Patients with symptoms of ischemic heart disease (angina pectoris), at an early age, should be examined from the cardiac side, usually with a coronarography examination of the coronary arteries. Postoperative follow-up should include intensives controls for the reason of the creation of pseudoaneurysm in the surgical suture lines.

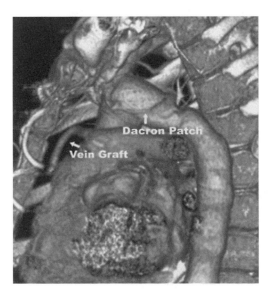

Fig. 81 _ Control CTA examination after the operation of the same patient – fig. 80 (Bardakci et al., 2007).

3.3.3.4 Wiskott-Aldrich syndrome

Wiskott-Aldrich syndrome (WAS) is a rare chromosomal recessive disease (linked to the X chromosome) characterised by skin eczema, throm-
bocytopenia, and immune deficiency with enteroragia. It is named after
the pediatrician, Robert Aldrich, who described it in a Dutch family after
immigration to the USA in 1954. A German paediatrician, Alfred Wiskott,
disease mentioned the disease for the first time in 1937 (Aldrich et al., 1954).
Some patients are affected by vasculitis that can cause an aneurysm of the
affected artery. Premature death comes as a result of a profound hemorrhage, infection, or a tumour disease. The diagnosis of the disease rests
in the clinical symptomatology and in the examination of the blood count.
A characteristic sign is the increased concentration of immunoglobulin
A and E (IgA, IgE) and low concentration of IgM (Radl et al., 1976).

The natural developments of the aneurysm of the thoracic aorta are
described by Narayan. Narayan described a 21 year old patient with a severe degree of aortic regurgitation with a dilated ascending aorta and root
(5.2cm). The aortic valve was bicuspid and the aortic root including the

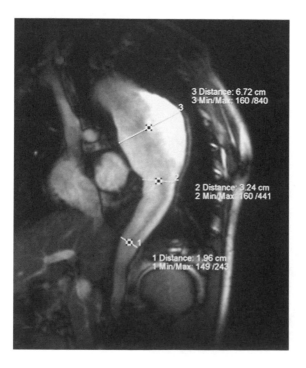

Fig. 82 _ Control
MRI in a patient
after operation
of the ascending
aorta. Dilation
of the aortic
arch and the
descending aorta
(Narayan et al.,
2004).

ascending aorta showed a severe degree of atherosclerotic involvement. In the first period, a replacement of the aortic root with a conduit (vascular prosthesis with a sewn valve replacement) was performed. During the follow-up three years later, an aneurysmal dilatation of the aortic arch and the descending aorta (6.4cm; Fig. 82) was found. For this reason, the patient underwent another cardiac surgical procedure, namely a total arch and descending aorta replacement. The histology of the excised aortic wall revealed a transmural chronic inflammatory process with infiltration of leucocytes, lymphocytes, plasma cells, and eosinophil cells (Narayan et al., 2004).

In this syndrome the thrombocytes are of a smaller size and have an insufficient function. Given the fact that they are increasingly uptaken and destructed in the spleen, their number is low. Blood transfusions, splenectomy, and bone marrow transplantation increases the rate of survival for patients. Some patients developed vasculitis, but it rarely affects the intermediates and the small arteries, for example the coronary arteries. Patients with WAS with symptoms of vasculitis should be followed for the reason of development of an aneurysm. Given the increased tendency of arterial dilatation, the regularity of the controls are important, and also in patients who were operated due to an aneurysm (Narayan et al., 2004).

3.3.3.5 Inflammatory diseases of the collagen – systemic lupus erythematosus and ankylosing spondylitis

Collagen diseases, ankylosing spondylitis (SA, Bechterew disease) and systemic lupus erythematosus (SLE) cause aortitis, that can lead to the development of an aneurysm more frequently in the ascending andabdominal aorta.

SLE plays a role in the mechanism of the development of the aneurysm of the aorta in the presence of atherosclerotic changes and vasculitis of the aortic wall, which is potentiated by the use of steroids (Chang et al., 2004).

The diagnosis of this disease is established on the basis of the examinations of a TEE, CTA, and MRI (Fig. 83). The disease of SLE usually comes with the development of vasculitis of small arteries, for example coronary, that is why the coronary disease is one of the main causes of death in young patients with SLE. Other worsening factors for patients with coronary diseases are arterial hypertension, hyperlipidemia, nephritic syndrome, and the chronic treatment with corticosteroids. These aneurysms have a high risk for complications. From the literature it is known that an aneurysm with a diametre from 3 to 6cm shows a high risk for rupture. That is why

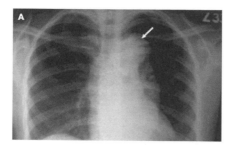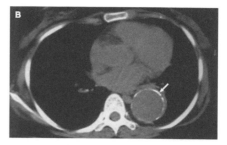

Fig. 83 _ Rontgen (left) and CT examination in a patients with aneurysm of the descending aorta in SLE (Chang et al., 2004).

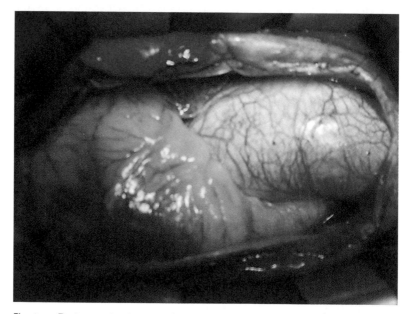

Fig. 84 _ Perioperative image of a patient with aneurysmal dilatation of the Ascending Aorta and Root in Bechterew disease (Sabol, 2010).

early preventive surgical procedures in patients with this systemic disease is recommended (Chang et al., 2004).

Ankylosing spondylitis is a chronic inflammatory disease that affects the sacroiliac and intervertebral joints of the spine. This is a disease that is typical by its progression, and as a result leads to the progressive synostosis and immobility of the spine. It is associated with the presence of HLA B27 (in more than 90% of the cases). The disease affects three times more men and its incidence in the population is 0.5%. In the beginning phases of the disease are dominated by symptoms from the joint involvement. In the extra-joint manifestations are frequent inflammation of the tendon, eye symptoms (chronic iridocyclitis), and lung involvement (restriction of the respiratory excursion, interstitial lung fibrosis). A late manifestation in some patients is the insufficiency of the aortic valve, that its essence is the dilatation of the aortic root (Fig. 84) or annuloaortic ectasia with fibrotic changes that can pass to the valve leaflet (aortic, mitral).

3.3.3.6 Inflammatory bowel disease (IBD)-ulcerative colitis

Ulcerative colitis is a disease that causes inflammation of the mucous membrane of the large bowel and anus. It leads to frequent hemorrhagic diarrhea, tenesmus, and spastic pain in the abdominal area and overall fatique. The manifestation of the disease is different according to how large part of

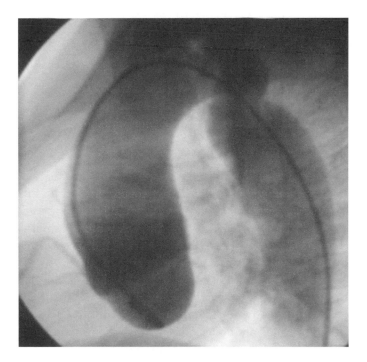

Fig. 85 _ Aortography of an Aneurysmal Ascending Aorta and Descending Aorta in ulcerative colitis (Karakurt et al., 2007).

the large bowel is affected. Symptoms over time change – there are chang-
ing periods of recurrence and remissions. In the heart complications of
the ulcerative colitis belong the myocarditis, pericarditis, increased risk of
infective endocarditis and sporadic aneurysm of the aorta (Fig. 85) (Karakurt
et al., 2007).

The cardiac surgical intervention for the removal of the aneurysm of
the aorta is planned after the regression of the inflammation with the treatment of prednisone and sulphasalazine.

3.3.3.7 Cogan's syndrome

Cogan's syndrome (CS) is a rare rheumatic disease that is usually found in
young people with an average age of 32 years old with the epicentre of the
incidence in the Caucasus. It is found in both genders. It is characterised by
the inflammatory involvement of the eyes (Interstitial Keratitis) and inner
ear with symptoms like photophobia, vertigo, and deafness. It can also be
present in symptoms of dilated vasculitis. The literature describes less than
250 cases of this disease.

Typical Cogan's syndrome has these symptoms:

a) eyes (Medial Keratitis);
b) ear (symptoms from the involvement of the statoacustic apparatus simi-
    lar like the Meniere's syndrome);
c) time intervals during which there is a clinical manifestation of the dis-
    ease is less than the two years.

O'Hayes suggests to perform a diagnosis of atypical CS in cases when
the eye symptoms are different from the medial keratitis and the time interval of the manifestation of the symptoms is longer than two years. Atypical CS is connected with other systemic diseases, for example, sarcoidosis, rheumatoid arthritis, Sjogren syndrome, inflammatory diseases of the
bowel, and Wegener granulomatosis.

The etiology of CS is unknown. In some cases, one of the possible trig-
ger factors is an infectious process, for example, rhinitis or pharyngitis,
tracheobronchitis, pneumonia from chlamydia, and others. Rheumatoid
factor and antinuclear antibodies are usually negative. Autoantibodies
against the cells of the endothelium of the inner eye and the cornea that
are found in some patients can provide an explanation for the etiology of
the autoimmune disease.

Except the mentioned symptoms, during the first two months from the outbreak of the disease, also non-specific symptoms (fever, fatique, weight loss) and symptoms from the involvement of the mobility and gastrointestinal system begin to manifest. The same neurological and skin disorders with lymphadenopathy, nefrititis, and orchititis are symptoms in the setting of the diagnosis of the disease.

From the cardiovascular symptoms, it is mainly aortitis that in 10% of the cases occurs with regurgitation of the aortic valve. The aortitis affects the whole aortic wall and is connected with a dilation (most frequently ascending) of the aorta. The microscopic findings are differentiated and characteristic. Aortitis in CS is not different from the aortitis in Takayasu disease. In some cases it is documented a presence of giant cells in the aortic wall.

Vascular complications can be found in the coronary vessels in the form of stenosis or aneurysmal dilatation with a clinical picture of myocardial ischemia to infarct. Documented also are complications, such as, pericarditis and rarely an involvement of the mitral valve.

The arteritis can be asymptomatic or is manifested as dyspnea, absence of the arterial wave, abdominal pain in mesenteric arteritis, intermittent claudications of the upper or lower limbs and/or renovascular arterial hypertension in stenosis of the renal artery.

The inflammatory process of the aortic wall can be manifested after years and this in the form of an aneurysm of the aorta. Described are some cases of the syndrome of the aortic arch. Corticosteroids are usually effective in the treatment of the eye, vascular or other symptoms from the abdominal organs, but they reach less reliable results in the involvement of the acustic apparatus. If the patient reacts positively to the treatment in 2 to 6 months, we gradually reduce the dose of the drugs. If the patient is resistant to the corticosteroid treatment, we use other immunosuppressive drugs, like the azathioprine, cyclophosphamide, cyclosporine, or methotrexate (Cochrane et al., 1991; Grasland et al., 2004).

3.3.3.8 Relapsing polychondritis

Relapsing polychondritis (RP) is an autoimmune chronic disease that affects the cartilage and other connective tissue, for example the elastic tissue of the heart valves and aortic wall. It is not a herediary type of disease. It is found in men and women, where the average age in the time of the establishment of the diagnosis is 40-50 years old. Were discovered autoimmune antibodies against collagen type II. Some association exists with rheumatologic diseases, for example systemic vasculitis, rheumatoid arthritis, SLE, and Sjogren syndrome (Dib et al., 2006).

Potential cardiac involvement is found in 15-40% of patients and includes an insufficiency of the aortic (AR) and mitral valve, myocarditis, pericarditis, conductive system, ischemia of the myocardium, dysrhythmia (atrial fibrillation, supraventricular tachycardia), aneurysm of the great arteries, and aorta. The heart involvement is the second most common cause of death after laryngo – tracheal complications.

The incidence of artic regurgitatiom (AR) is 4-6% and mitral insufficiency (MR) 2-3% in the spectrum of cardiac complications. Usually the AR is manifested later after the establishment of the clinical diagnosis of RP (approximately after 7 years) and as a result of the dilatation of the aortic root (in 78% of cases) or as a result of the involvement of the valve leaflet endocardium. There are also rapid progressive aortic aneurysms (2-3 months after the establishment of the diagnosis). Surgical intervention is recommended in the cases of symptomatic AR, when the aortic valve is often bicuspid. The incidence of MR is less frequent than the AR. Concomitant involvement of the aortic and mitral valve is also possible given the involvement of the valve leaflet endothelium; it is recommended for a replacement than a reconstructive procedure on the valve (Dib et al., 2006).

The etiology of MR in RP is diverse. It can be caused on the background of the dilatation of the mitral annulus, in the fibrous conversion, and retraction of the valve leaflets, as a result of the prolapse of the anterior leaflet and in the rupture of a primary chordae as a result of the endocarditis. On the basis from data from the professional literature from the total number of the patients, who needed a surgical intervention, 67% of them were men with an average age of 42.5 years old. The average time from the onset of the disease to the cardiac surgical procedure was 5.1 years. The histopathological finding from the removed tissue samples (valves, aortic wall) were cystic degeneration of the collagen with a decreased number of elastic fibers, significant decrease in the content of the mucopolysacharides, post-inflammatory fibrous involvement of the valve leaflet and myxomatoid degeneration. A replacement of the ascending valve (AVR) was performed on the majority of patients, in few patients with AVR with the replacement of the ascending aorta and root with a conduit (Bentall) and the rest of the patients underwent an aortic–mitral double-valve replacement. After the mentioned procedures (isolated AVR, MVR), a high percentage of paravalvular leaks was documentated. The authors state two reasons for the failure:

a) the traction of the Dacron ring of the artificial valve replacement on the post-inflammatory changed and fragile aorta around the valve replacement;

b) probable progression of the basic disease (RP), like in part of the aortic wall , and also on the aortic and mitral annulus.

These with the surgical associated complications occurred despite the treatment with corticosteroids. Patients with RP, who are indicated for AVR as a result of the dilatation of the ascending aorta or the root, it is recommended to directly perform a Bentall operation. Isolated AVR does not "treat" the post-inflammatory changed aorta and does not eliminate the risk of the aneurysm of the aortic root. Only in patients with only a valvular pathology without any macroscopic signs of involvement of the aorta can an isolated AVR be performed. For these patients is always indicated longterm immunosuppressive treatment (corticosteroids, immunosuppressives) and this also in the relative contraindication for the administration of corticosteroids, whose adverse effect is the deterioration of the strength of the heart tissue that has the higher risk for the development of a paravalvular leak. Currently, it was confirmed that there is a remission of the disease. Therefore postoperatively it is recommended to replace the corticosteroids with modern immunosupressives. This treatment can prevent potential complications, that can be mediastinitis, an acute paravalvular leak and others (Dib et al., 2006).

3.3.3.9 Reactive arthritis- Reiter syndrome (ReA)

In 1916, Hans Reiter described a classic triad: arthritis, urethritis, and menigococcal conjunctivitis.

Reactive arthritis (Reiter syndrome, ReA) is an acute aseptic arthritis that is often complicated by a secondary superinfection. The primary infection of the gastrointestinal or urogenital system cause after an interval of 2-6 weeks reactive arthritis (ReA). ReA is caused more often in HLA-B27 positive patients. Antigen HLA-B27 is often found (up to 95%) in patients with ankylosing spondylitis. The main symptom is monoarthritis, oligoarthritis predominantly with the involvement of the joints of the lower limbs. The pathogenesis of the disease is not fully elucidated. It is assumed that there is some interaction between the HLA-B27 of the host and some bacteria. Examples may be Shigella flexneri, Campylobacter jejuni, Salmonella species, Yersinia enterocolica and pseudotuberculosis, Chlamydia trachomatis, Clostidium difficile, and others. The ReA is stimulated by CD-8 positive T-cells that react to the peptides that are released from the bacteria, while they are attached to the HLA-B27. The incidence of the disease in the population is 46/100000 residents and the patient's age with this disease is usually 15-35 years old.

The clinical symptoms of the disease may be musculoskeletal, skin, urogenital, gastrointestinal ocular, and cardiovascular (Ceska).

In 1-2% of the patients occurs an insufficiency of the aortic valve (AR) as a result of the aseptic inflammation of the aortic wall that can lead to the development of an aneurysm of the aorta. More frequently disorders of the conductive system of the heart are found (Ceska, 2010).

3.3.3.10 Allergic granulomatosis (Churg-Strauss syndrome)

The basic units of this specific group of vasculitis that are associated with the presence of antibodies against the cytoplasma of the neutrophile leucocytes (ANCA) are three clinical units:

a) Wegener granulomatosis
b) Microscopic polyangitis
c) Churg-Strauss syndrome (CHSsy).

These units affect the cardiovascular system more frequently the CHSsy. This is a very rare systemic disease that is characterised by the association of asthma, eosinophilia, vasculitis, and extragranular granuloms (migrating lung infiltrates). The incidence in the population is 2.4-4 in 1000000 residents; affects patients from the age of 4 to 75 years old with an average age of 50 years old. CHSsy is not a hereditary or an infectious disease.

The etiology of the syndrome is not known, but there is a presence of asthma, eosinophilia, and increased levels of IgE prove autoimmune allergic processes. Some authors claim that at the same time there is the presence of an increased sensitivity to drugs, like penicillin, mesalazine, and the modificators of the leucotrienes (Ceska, 2010).

The disease proceeds in three consecutive phases:

1. First phase is characterised by the occurrence of asthma with or without an allergic rhinitis;
2. During the second phase comes the development of peripheral eosinophilia and infiltration of the eosinophils into the ligaments, that is manifested either as the Loeffler's syndrome or as an eosinophilic inflammation of the lung or as a gastroenteritis;

3. The third phase includes different organ systems. It is life threatening and painful. It is characterised by a vasculitis that effects whichever organ, where the involvement of the heart is directly life threatening. The clinical manifestations of the heart involvement include chest pain (like in angina pectoris) and dyspnea. The vasculitis also negatively affects the lung, kidney, liver, and gastrointestinal tract. It can lead to aortitis and later to the development of an aneurysm of the aorta. (Vogel et al., 1992).

The American rheumatologic society (1990) introduced six criteria for the diagnosis of CHSsy, which are:

1. Asthma;
2. Eosinophilia-more than 10% of eosinophils in blood count;
3. Mononeuropathy or polyneuropathy;
4. Volatile lung migratory infiltrates (not fixed) on the background of vasculitis;
5. Involvement of the paranasal sinuses-history of acute or chronic pain or increased sensitivity in the area;
6. Extravascular eosinophil infiltrates on the basis of biopsy samples of arteries or venules with the present of infiltrates (vessels with the cell nucei extravascular).

The diagnosis of the disease is thus based on the significant eosinophilia, anemia, high sedimentation and often positive ANCA p-type.

In summary based on the results of a study by Chau et al., in 13 patients, who had a finding of aseptic aortitis, one can draw the following conclusions:

1. The regurgitation of the aortic valve (AR) with aortitis in Takayasu arthritis has a worse prognosis than the aortitis of other etiology;
2. The aortitis, we diagnose if
   a) significant thickening of the aortic wall;
   b) on an echocardiographic examination there is a gradual dilatation of the ascending aorta and the aortic root;
   c) constant high levels of imflammation parametres without signs of sepsis of infectious process. It is important to establish a diagnosis because of the high risk of failure (paravalvular leak) of a future prosthetic valve (54%). After the diagnosis of the disease the treatment continues with the application of immunosuppressive drugs (corticosteroids – prednisone, immunosupressives – azathioprin,

cyclophosphamide) and frequent monitoring of the inflammation parametres, where the level of the CRP (C-reactive protein) should decrease below 20. After the cardiac surgical intervention it is necessary to follow it with an anti-inflammatory treatment for the purpose of decreasing the potential surgical complications (paravalvular leak, suture line dehiscence, suture line aneurysm);

3. The total replacement of the aortic root is the most suitable treatment in patients with AR as a result from an aortitis. If the surgical intervention is limited to an isolated replacement and/or ascending aorta, the reoperation risk reaches 59% per year versus the Bentall operation where the risk is significant lower at 20% per year. The Bentall operation can be used as a conduit with a mechanical valve or a cryopreserved aortic homograft, where in its use the tension on the anastomosis site is probably less and that is why there is less risk of suture line dehiscence or the development of an aneurysm in the suture line (Chau et al., 2006).

3.3.3.11 Sarcoidosis

Sarcoidosis is a systemic inflammatory disease with an incidence of 10 to 40/100000 people per year. The most frequently affected organ is the lung, but the systemic inflammation often attacks the musculoskeletal system, skin, central nervous system, and the cardiovascular apparatus. In the tissue, we find granulomas in which at centre are macrophages, epithelial cells, multinucleated giant cells, and activated CD4 lymphocytes. In their periphery are fibroblasts, macrophages and CD4 and CD8 activated lymphocytes.

The vasculitis is rareply present in sarcoidosis. It has not been confirmed that the vasculitis is the real manifestation of the primary disease, or that it is present as a coincidential abnormality. In the professional literature, there are only few studies concerning the co-existence of sarcoidosis and the vasculitis (aortitis). Redenbacher presented the only case report of a patient with aortitis with histologic changes that are similar to the changes we see in Takayasu arteritis or in sarcoidosis. After the histologic examination they established the diagnosis of "TA-like" disease.

It is not always possible to differentiate TA from sarcoidosis, this can be the result of a common etiopathogenetic mechanism of both diseases (Weiter et al., 2000).

3.3.3.12 Idiopathic isolated aortitis

This diagnosis defines a non-infectious inflammation of the aorta without current involvement of its branches. The incidence, similar like the pathogenesis are not known. The result of the untreated form of the disease is the dilatation and the aneurysm of the aorta. The existence of the disease is proven by the examination of autopsy and biopsy samples of the wall of the aorta.

Royo-Levya in his study examined 1204 samples of the aorta. In 88% of the cases, the reason for cardiac surgery was an aneurysm or a dissection of the aorta. In 36 cases (3%) an idiopathic aortitis was diagnosed. In approximately 2/3 of the cases samples came from women. In 16 cases, the histopathological picture found giant cells similar to the findings in GCA. This may support an opinion that it is a focal form of GCA, that it is located on the aortic arch. However no patient manifested clinical symptoms of the disease GCA (Royo-Levya et al., 2000).

In the last period, it is more often described a picture of isolated aortitis in the examination of the positron emission tomography with the use of 18-fluorodeoxyglucose (FDG-PET) if patients have a fever of unknown origin. The examination has more diagnostic sensitivity than the other imaging methods (CTA, ultrasound) whose results may be false negative. It is probable that the increasing availability of the PET will lead to the growth of the diagnosis of this disease (Zalts et al., 2005).

3.3.3.13 Ormond's disease

Idiopathic retroperitoneal fibrosis (IRF) is a rare disease with an incidence in 0.2-1/100000 people. It is characterised by the development of fibrous tissue periaortic and around the iliac vessel. The background is an inflammation that is based on the adventitia (chronic periaortitis) of the abdominal aorta and the iliac arteries, that its result is massive production of ligaments. In the retroperitoneum it causes oppression in the anatomical structures, like the ureters and the vena cava inferior. Etiologically is considered an excessive inflammatory reaction in topical atherosclerotic changes. On the other hand, present are systemic symptoms and increased levels of inflammatory parametres that creates a logical assumption for an auto-immune process. The competence to vasculitis confirms the findings from FDG-PET examination, when in the area of the abdominal aorta is imaged an increased metabolic activity of glucose as a result of the inflammatory process. Finding similar like in the case of the idiopathic isolated aortitis, is a similar picture of giant cell arteritis (GCA). Up to 50% of cases present an involvement of the aortic arch and epiaortic arteries (Vaglio et al., 2003; Salvarani et al., 2005).

In IRF mainly men after the age of 50 years old are affected. The initial clinical manifestation is non-specific – fever, fatique and increased sweating appear. Later, an added pain in the abdominal region as a result of the involvement of the retroperitoneal organs is included (van Bommel et al., 2002).

3.3.4 Aneurysms in arterial hypertension and atherosclerosis

The main risk factors for the development of an aneurysm of the aorta are arterial hypertension and atherosclerosis. In cases of an aortic aneurysm the wall of the aorta has severe atherosclerotic plaques in 90% of the cases and more than the 75% of the patients suffer from chronic hypertensive disease, most often not adequately treated (Cohn, 2011; Kouchoukos, 2012).

The long term increase of blood pressure causes a total rebuilding of the vessel wall-thickening the intima, fibrosis, calcification and extracellular storage of fatty acids. The radial pressure leads to accelerated degeneration, elastolysis with hyalinisation of the collagen. These mechanisms can come from the disruption to the rupture of the intima, mainly in its most vulnerable place, at the edges of the atherosclerotic plaques. The thickening of the intima and the fibrosis of the adventitia, like the destruction of the vasa vasorum leads to the worsening blood circulation of the wall that leads to further deepening of the structural changes that lead to the development of necrosis of the smooth muscle cells of the lamina media. Persistent high blood pressure, increased tension on the vessel wall and weakening of its layers create a predisposition to the development of an aneurysm. As a risk factor it is essential to also state smoking and hypercholesterolemia, where its effect is associated mainly with the development of atherosclerosis and hypertension (Nienaber et al., 2003).

3.3.5   Aneurysms with an infectious etiology

"Mycotic" aneurysms of the aorta are caused by an inflammatory process that is happens during total body infection. The cause of the aneurysm of the aorta is the destruction of the media of the aortic wall. Osler was the first that used the term "mycotic" in which he described a finding of fresh fungal bodies on the surface of the intima of an aortic aneurysm in a patient with an infective endocarditis.

This reference was presented in the lectures about endocarditis that were done at the Royal College of Physicians (The Gulstonian lectures) in London in 1885, where a case report of a young man with multiple infectious aneurysms of the ascending aorta in bacterial endocarditis was described. Since than the term "mycotic" is used for all the types of infectious aneurysms despite that the fungi are responsible only for a small percentage of the aneurysms of the aorta (Long et al., 1999).

In the "pre-antibiotic" era the main cause of an infectious aneurysm of the aorta was by hematogenic spread infective endocarditis. The aneurysms of an infectious etiology represents 0.7%-2.6% of all aortic aneurysms. Risk groups are diabetics and patients with a decreased immunity (after therapy with corticosteroids, after chemotherapy, in IV drug users, HIV positivity). Also surgical procedures in the medical history (aortic surgery, aortocoronary bypass grafting) represent some risk for the patient (Cohn, 2011; Raupach et al., 2005). The patients usually do not have characteristic symptoms and the diagnosis is established already after the rupture of the aneurysm or in the advanced state of the sepsis. It is known there is a high tendency to rupture, in the basis of autopsy and also biopsy samples the risk of rupture of the aneurysm is in the range of 53%-75% (Long et al., 1999).

Mechanisms for the development of infectious aneurysm of the aorta (Cohn, 2011):

1. The infective agent directly attracks the intima – hematogenically spreading. In the physiologic conditions the intima of the aorta is resistant against the infections. However if it is primarily destructed by an atherosclerotic process (ulcerogenesis), it leads to the disruption of the integrity of the intima and to the colonisation of the wall of the aorta by the agent;
2. The agents colonise the media and the adventitia of the aortic wall through the vasa vasorum;
3. Direct or indirect spread through the lymphatic system from the primary source of infection (from the lymphatic nodes-abcess);
4. Into the aortic wall the agents enter after trauma or iatrogenic.

The most frequent pathogen is Staphylococcus aureus (53%) and Salmonella enteritis (30%) and less frequent agents are Streptococcus species, Proteus mirabilis, and Clostridium septicum.

The infectious diseases that can cause aortitis or aneurysm of the aorta includes:

1. Tuberculosis;
2. Salmonellosis;
3. Syphilis;
4. Staphylococcal infections;
5. Clostridial infection;
6. Streptococcal infection;
7. Chagas disease;
8. Acquired Immune Deficiency Syndrome (AIDS);
9. Other infectious agents that can cause aneurysm of the aorta.

The infectious agents of the aneurysms can be divided into four types:

1. Primary inflammatory aneurysm;
2. Secondary infectious aneurysm in bacterial endocarditis;
3. Infected atherosclerotic aneurysm;
4. Post-traumatic infected false aneurysm.

3.3.5.1 Tuberculosis

The first case of tuberculous aortitis was recorded in 1882 by Weigert and the first reported case of a "mycotic:" tuberculous aneurysm was presented in 1895. Since 1945, there have only been 19 recorded cases of an aneurysm of the thoracic aorta.

In the pathogenesis of the tuberculous aneurysms includes the first three above mentioned mechanisms. In 75% of cases the infection directly passes from the infectious source for example abcesses in the paravertebral lymphatic nodes in the tuberculosis of the lungs. Haythorn described four types of tuberculous vascular disease:

a) milliary tuberculosis of the intima of the arteria;
b) tuberculous polyps on the intima of the arteria;
c) tuberculosis that affect the vessel wall transmurally;
d) tuberculous aneurysm.

Prior to the discovery of antituberculous drugs, the last two types of the disease were more frequently found. The rupture of the wall (Fig. 87, 88) from an infection of the affected artery can be caused either in the field of an aneurysm or the rupture happens before the development of an aneurysm.

At the same time studies from India describe another pathophysiologic mechanism and pathologic picture of the involvement of the aorta and its branches, when it comes to the stenotisation up to the obliteration of the artery in young patients with tuberculosis, where the cause is the hypersensitivity of the organism (allergic reaction) to the tuberculous antigens. Most frequently the aneurysm is false (pseudoaneurysm; Fig. 86). The professional literature described only sporadic cases of the development of a true aneurysm in tuberculosis. The false aneurysm anatomically presents a perivascular hematoma that communicates with the artery through a neck and is characterised by a sudden development.

In the vast majority of publications about the tuberculous aneurysm, the infectious agent was the bacteria – Mycobacterium tuberculosis.

The tuberculous aneurysms show these characteristic signs:

a) permanent pain in the thoracic (mainly dorsal) and abdominal region;
b) severe bleeding into the lung parenchyma and pleura, in the gastrointestinal tract, into the retroperitoneal or pericardial cavity;
c) a para-aortic "tumorous" mass can be detected by palpation or by a standard roentgen examination – static shot in an expansion process or a dynamic shot in localisations near the heart.

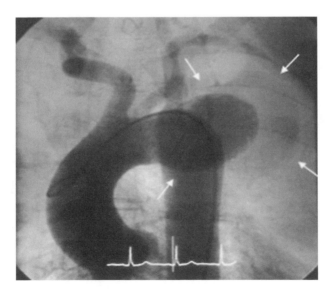

Fig. 86 _ Aortography of a false Aneurysm (pseudoaneurysm) of the Descending Aorta in tuberculosis (Suresh et al., 2003).

Up to 38% of cases of tuberculosis in the asymptomatic course of the aneurysm is not microbiologically diagnosed. These aneurysm are called "cryptogenic" aneurysms and appear in the non-presence of infectious locus of tuberculosis (Bojar et al., 1998; Suresh et al., 2003).

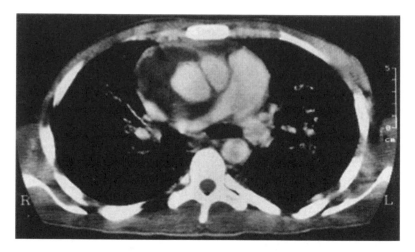

Fig. 87 _ CTA examination of a Dissection of the Ascending Aorta with a thrombus in tuberculosis (Bojar et al., 1998).

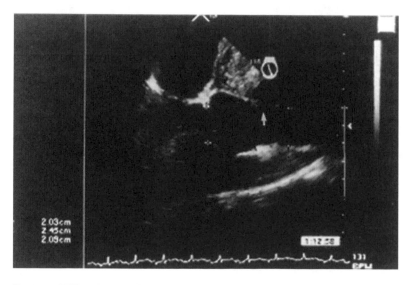

Fig. 88 _ TEE with an infectious process (tuberculosis), damaged wall of the Ascending Aorta (arrow) (Bojar et al., 1998).

3.3.5.2 Salmonellosis

The bacteria of the family called Salmonela can cause five main diseases that due to diagnostic reasons we divide into five categories:
1. Gastroenetritis;
2. Bowel fever;
3. Bacteremia;
4. Local infection;
5. Chronic microbiophoria.

From the local complications the most severe are vasculitis, myelitis, and meningitis. Vascular complications are seen in the region of the thoracic and abdominal aorta, and also in the coronary vessels. Nearly all of the aortitis lead to the development of an aneurysm. The majority of patients that are affected by aortitis from the Salmonella species have as a predisposing factor already developed atherosclerotic involvement in the infectious field. The patients are most male (men are three times more often) with an average age >60 years old. Nearly one fourth of the patients have diabetes. The aneurysms of the thoracic aorta are found in 17% of the patients with this infectious disease.

In the majority of the patients comes to the manifestation of the disease subacute with an average time of duration of the symptoms about one month. The main symptoms are fever, rigor, and symptoms connected with the primary site of the infection, for example diarrhea. In the thoracic aneurysm 17-21% of patients complain of chest pain, in the abdominal and dorsal region or the disease is manifested as a dyspnea. In isolated cases comes the creation of an aorto-bronchial fistula with hemoptysis.

In the majority of patients (up to 85%) there is a positive finding of an infectious agent in their blood; in 65% of cases there is a finding also in their stool. The microorganisms that cause this disease are: S. typhimurium and S. enteritidis.

The complications that occur in the thoracic aneurysm are the aortopulmonary fistula, pneumonia, and aosteomyelitis of the sternum (Lin et al., 2003; Karakurt et al., 2007).

3.3.5.3 Syphilis

Cardiovascular syphilis (syphilitic aneurysm of the aorta) is a rare diagnosis. Worldwide, literature only records several dozen of cases since the advent of the antibiotic era. Most frequently, it occurs in the dilatation of the ascending aorta, less frequently it is dilated the aortic annulus or stenotic involvement of the coronary vessels.

Syphilitic aneurysm is often symptomatic (Fig. 89, 91). It can erode the sternum and on palpation paravertebrally is present a pulsative mass (Fig. 90).

This clinical picture happens in the tertiary stage of lues. The infection is caused by a microorganism called Treponema pallidum. All patients with syphilitic aortitis have a positive serologic test (Chockalingam et al., 2004; Varna et al., 2009).

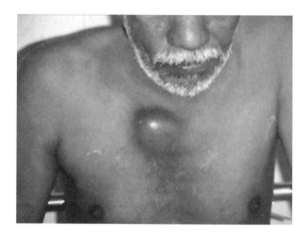

Fig. 89 _ Patient with a luetic aneurysm of the aorta (Chochalingam et al., 2004).

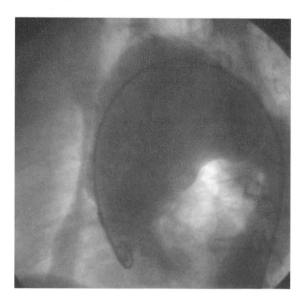

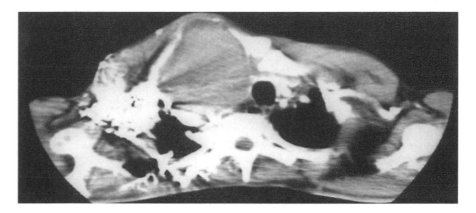

Fig. 90 _ Aneurysm of the Ascending Aorta and Innominate artery eroding the sternum and the thoracic wall (Varna et al., 2006).

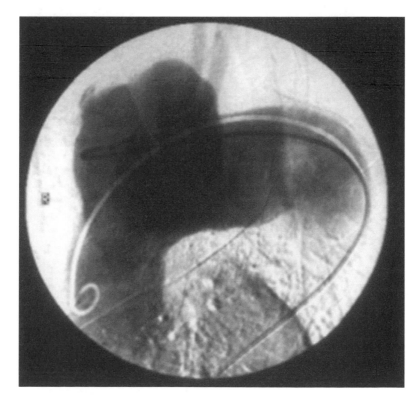

Fig. 91 _ Aortographia showing a gigantic saccular Aneurysm (luetic) of the Thoracic Aorta with an involvement of the Innominate artery (Varna et al., 2006).

3.3.5.4 Staphylococcal infection

In the professional literature, it described cases of "mycotic" aneurysms of the descending aorta, where the etiologic agent was Staphylococcus aureus sensitive or resistant to methicillin (MRSA-Methicillin Resistant Staphylococcus Aureus) (Fig. 92; Munakata et al., 2004).

Johansen indicates that an immunosuppressive state, as a result of alcoholism, diabetes, and chronic renal failure is a predisposition factor for the development of a "mycotic" aneurysm. The atherosclerotic involvement of the wall of the aorta facilitates the bacterial infiltration and contamination (Johansen et al., 1983).

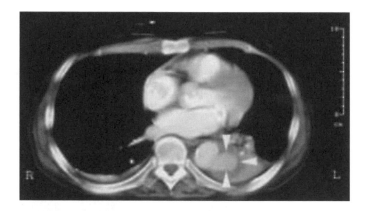

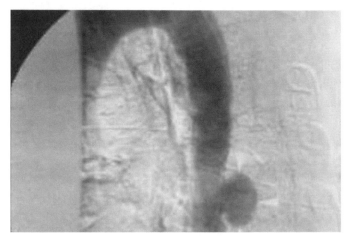

Fig. 92 _ CTA and angiography of a "mycotic" pseudoaneurysm of the descending aorta (Munakata et al., 2004).

Two pathophysiologic mechanisms are described:

1) local spreading of the infection from the site of the infection, for instance from the bronchi;
2) septic microembolisation to the vasa vasorum of the wall of the aorta.

The aneurysms generally have a very bad prognosis with a high risk of septic shock and rupture of the aneurysm. It is appropriately to postpone the surgical intervention to the "mycotic" aneurysm, until the systemic infection (antibiotics) is eliminated. Ruptures or incipient ruptures indicate the need for an urgent operation (Munakata et al., 2004; Verbrugge et al., 2006).

3.3.5.5 Clostridial infection

The incidence of the infectious aneurysm caused by the clostridium septicum iis very sporadic. This bacteria rarely causes an infection in human (opportunistic pathogen). It may cause myonecrosis and in the majority of cases it is responsible for infections in patients with an adenocarcinoma of the bowel. In the literature, it described saccular aneurysms of the aortic arch with extension to the descending aorta. Except from classic complications, the aneurysm can be complicated with the creation of an aortopulmonary fistula.

Treatment includes high initial doses of antibiotics with a gradual decrease and long term maintenance treatment. Surgical intervention consist of the conventional excision of the "mycotic" aneurysm if possible and, the extra-anatomical reconstruction of the arterial system (Braham et al., 1990).

3.3.5.6 Steptococcal infection

In the last 25 years, in only 20 cases, data exists about an infectious aneurysm of the aorta (usually the descending) that is caused by a streptococcal infection (Streptococcus pneumoniae). The prognosis for these patients is not good.

The mechanism of the development of the aneurysm is the called per migrationem – an expansion of the infection from the lung lesion directly to the aortic wall.

The treatment is composed of conservative antibiotic part and a surgical operation. Its essence is a radical excision that reaches a healthy area of the aortic wall and replaces the affected part of the aorta with a prosthetic implantation or allogenic homograft (Pasic et al., 1999; Nijs et al., 2002).

3.3.5.7 Chagas disease – "megaorgans"

Chagas disease, known also as an American Trypanosomiasis is a tropical parasitic disease that is caused by the protozoa Trypanosoma cruzi that is transmitted by the bug's bite. The infected bug transmits the infection only during the bite releases its infected feces. Possible also is the transmission by blood from human to human (transfusion, transplantation, pregnancy). The incubation time is one to four weeks. The main target organ that the parasite attacks is the bowel, heart, and brain (spastic state). The course can be acute or chronic. Initially often present is an eye infection (conjunctivitis) with edema of the eyelids and a lymphadenopathy (swelling of the local lymph nodes). This is the classic triad of symptoms called Romana syndrome (Fig. 93). In the acute phase (parasite is in the blood circulation) fever, dyspnea, and abdominal pain are present. After the acute phase the chronic phase begins, that can last for years. During this phase, comes the serious involvement of the heart, bowel, and CNS. The results are often fatal.

In the heart involvement we talk about myocarditis and dilatation of the heart chambers (aneurysms of the right and left heart ventricles), including dilatation of the coronary vessels that can lead to thromboembolic complications and myocardial ischemia (Fig. 94). In very rare cases may be a dilatation of the aorta, respectively the development of the megaaorta. The result of the cardiac involvement may be sudden cardiac death, dysrhythmia, and embolisation or rupture of the dilated aorta (Texeira et al., 2006).

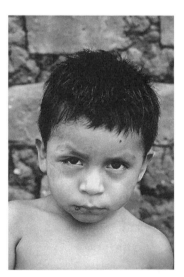

Fig. 93 _ A child from Panama with a Chagas disease with an oedematous right eye (Romana symptom) (this picture is a work of a worker of the Center for Disease Control and Prevention, that is a part of the United States Department of Health and Human Services, that was created as a part of his employment. As a work of the federal government of the USA, this picture is a free piece of work).

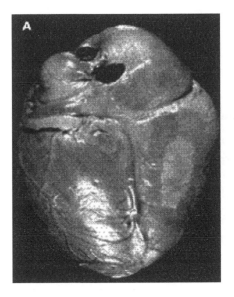
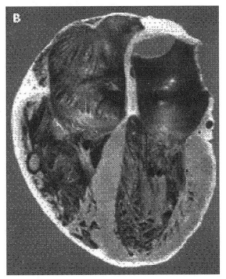

Fig. 94 _ Autopsy samples of the chronic form of the Chagas disease. (A) bleached spots of the inferior wall of LV and dilated coronary vessels; (B) dilated rightside and leftside heart chambers (Texeira et al., 2006).

In the case of bowel involvement comes the destruction of the ganglion cells in the bowel wall that as a final result causes a loss of the peristalsis and the creation of the megacolon and megaesophagus. Without an operation the patients dies as a result of the perforation and peritonitis.

Treatment is effective only in the acute phase (Nifurtimox, Benzidazol), where vaccination against the disease do not exist (Longo, 2011).

3.3.5.8 Acquired immune deficiency syndrom (AIDS)

The relationship between the Human Immunodeficiency Virus and aneurysm development has been described in scientific literature.

Common traits observed in aneurysm patients with HIV or AIDS:

a) Patient of a young age;
b) Absent or minimal atherosclerotic involvement of the arteries;
c) Necrotising granulomatous vasculitis with rapidly growing aneurysm and increased risk of rupture.

With HIV-infected patients, typical sites of aneurysm formation are common carotid arteries, thoracic and abdominal aorta; and the common iliac, femoral and popliteal arteries. The aneurysms are of saccular form and may develop concurrently in multiple segments of the aorta and its branches (Fig. 95).

Two phatological-anatomical findings are described in the aortic wall:

a) Neoangiogenesis as a result of an autoimmune reaction;
b) Necrotizing vasculitis of intense degree with the formation of aneurysm, caused by a local infection of the vessel wall or by thrombosis. Cultivation of samples from the vessel wall is mostly negative (Chello et al., 2002).

Patients with multiple aneurysms can be treated using either open surgery (conventional excision and replacement) or endovascular stent-graft implantation (thoracic endovascular aortic repair – TEVAR). Indications for surgical or interventional treatment of aneurysm are identical to treatment of aneurysm of other etiologies. Preoperative antibiotic treatment is also recommended (Heikkinen et al., 2005).

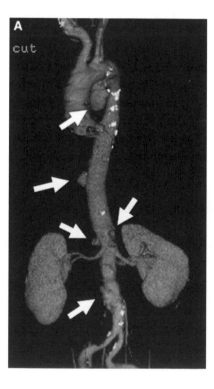

Fig. 95 _ CTA imaging of multiple aneurysms of the aorta in a HIV positive patient (Heikkinen et al., 2005).

3.3.5.9 Other infectious agents that cause aneurysm of the aorta

Microorganisms that can on rare occasions cause aortitis or mycotic aneurysm include:

1. *Pseudomonas aeruginosa* in immunosuppressed patients;
2. *Chlamydia pneumoniae*;
3. *Listeria monocytogenes*;
4. *Escherichia coli;*
5. *Haemophilus influenzae.*

To address infectious aneurysms and related diagnostic methods, Macedo et al researched the archives of the Mayo Clinic in the United States and authored a scientific paper about infectious aneurysms from records obtained over a 25-year period. The authors suggested that the method of choice for the diagnosis of infectious aortic aneurysms is a PET-CT scan. Alternatively, conventional angiography or isolated MRA can be used. The most common form of infectious aneurysm is the saccular form (Macedo et al. 2004).

Thoracic aortic aneurysms can form various fistulae with surrounding organs, including formation of an aorto bronchial, aorto-esophageal or aorto-pulmonary fistula. These fistulas are significant in the diagnosis of infectious aneurysms.

3.4 Clinical Symptoms of Aortic Aneurysm

Clinical symptomatology of aortic aneurysms can be very poor. Aneurysms can be diagnosed coincidentally during a lung X-Ray or echocardiogram procedures. Enlargement of the aneurysm can lead to exerted pressure on surrounding structures and cause the following symptoms: pain (retrosternal, radiating to shoulder and neck) or pressure on the superior vena cava, trachea or laryngeal recurrent nerve. Some degree of aortic valve regurgitation can often be present. At times, dissection or rupture is the first symptom of aneurysm.

In aneurysms of the ascending aorta, pain often radiates to the ventral side of the chest. The pain can be acute indicating impending rupture of the aneurysm or chronic caused by constant pressure of the aneurysm on the sternum. Symptoms of superior vena cava and respiratory structures obstruction can also be present. Less commonly, aneurysms of the ascending aorta or the aortic root can manifest by a rupture of the right coronary sinus or fistulation of the superior vena cava, causing cardiac tamponade or heart failure. Fistulation and bleeding to the lungs results in hemoptysis. Compression of the laryngeal recurrent nerve causes hoarseness (in up to 5% of cases).

As much as 57% of patients with degenerative aortic aneurysms of the descending aorta have clinical symptoms and as many as 9% of cases result in aneurysm rupture. A typical symptom in cases of descending thoracic aortic aneurysms is interscapular back pain. Large thoracic aneurysms formed in the *hiatus diaphragmaticus* are accompanied by epigastric pain. Additional clinical symptoms resulting from the close distance of the aneurysm to the surrounding structures are presented in Table 11 (Cohn, 2011).

A very serious aortic aneurism complication is dissection (see Chapter 4). A rare syndrome related to aortic aneurysm is Ortner's syndrome, which

CLINICAL SYMPTOMS	Asymptomatic
	Symptomatic (depending on aortic aneurysm location)
	• Aortic valve regurgitation symptoms
	• Pressure pain (retrosternal, intrascapular, epigastric, etc.)
	• Symptoms due to obstruction of surrounding structures
	– Superior vena cava syndrome
	– dyspnoe, cough (tracheal obstruction)
	– Hoarseness (obstruction of the recurrent laryngeal nerve)
	– Dyspaghia aortica (compression of the esophagus)
	– Neurological dysfunction and spinal balance disorders (compression of the spinal cord and vertebrae)
	• Fistula formation with surrounding organs and structures
	– With Superior vena cava (severe hemodynamic compromise, cardiac volume overload)
	– With the bronchial tree (hemoptysis)
	– With the GIT – duodenum (melena, **hematemesis**)
	• Peripheral embolization (thrombotic and atherosclerotic material from the aneurysm wall)
	Symptomatic due to rupture
	• Aortic aneurysm dissection
	• Rupture, most often of the right coronary sinus (cardiac tamponade)

Tab. 11 _ Clinical Symptomatology of Aortic Aneurysm (Cohn, 2011)

was first described in 1897 as a left recurrent laryngeal nerve palsy due to cardiovascular diseases, and is therefore also called a cardio-vocal syndrome. The cardiovascular causes of Ortner's syndrome include aortic aneurysm, dilation of left atrium due to mitral stenosis and pulmonary hypertension.

Another possible complication related to aortic aneurysms is *dysphagia aortica*. It is presented by atypical symptoms, typically by dysphagia and non-specified chest pain due to compression of the esophagus by the aneurysmal sac. It can be present in cases of descending aortic aneurysms of atherosclerotic origin or with connective tissue disorders (Marfan syndrome, etc.). The first mention of dysphagia aortica in relation to thoraco-abdominal aneurysms was presented by De Pape in 1932. Diagnostic methods of choice are CT angiography and esophagography procedures.

3.5 Aortic Aneurysm Diagnostic Methods

The basic and most wide spread examinations for aneurysms are echocardiography and spiral CT angiography using contrast material. Additional examination methods include magnetic resonance imaging, intravascular ultrasound imaging technology or a less often used positron emission tomography (PET) scan. The past 'gold standard' for diagnosis of aortic aneurysms, aortography, is currently only used marginally (see detailed description in Chapter 2).

3.6 Aortic Aneurysm Treatment

Depending on the specific indication criteria, patient age, associated diseases and size of the aneurysm, surgery, endovascular, or conservative treatment is indicated (Tab. 12).

SURGERY	• Connection of a patient to extra-corporeal circuit (ECC) • Cardiac or Circulatory arrest (temporarily cessation of the ECC) • Aneurysm replacement using tubular vascular prosthesis
ENDOVASCULAR TREATMENT	• Suitable with distal aortic dissection from left subclavian artery, and with hybrid procedure of arch aneurysm (including surgical debranching) • Implantation of the stentgraft into the aortic lumen (false lumen obturation and closure of the entry tear) • Lower periprocedural risk for patients in comparison to traditional surgical intervention
DISEASE MANAGEMENT (PHARMACOLOGIC TREATMENT)	• With asymptomatic aneurysms • In high risk polymorbid patients • Treatment of arterial hypertension (beta blockers, antihypertensive drugs, anti-impulse treatment)

Tab. 12 _ Aortic Aneurysm Treatment (Sabol, 2011).

3.6.1 Surgical Treatment of Aortic Aneurysm

Open surgical treatment of aortic diseases is based on replacement of the affected tissue section with a vascular prosthesis. In the case of ascending aortic and/or aortic arch aneurysm, the patient is connected to an extra-corporeal circuit and the heart is stopped by the administration of cardioplegia solution. The affected section of the aorta is removed and a tubular prosthesis is implanted in its place (Fig. 96A, 96B). In cases of descending or abdominal aortic aneurysm repair, the heart is not arrested.

Aneurysms can affect the ascending aorta, aortic arch, descending aorta, or in rare cases the entire aorta. Mortality for elective isolated ascending aorta replacement is not high (1-2%), similar to aortic root replacement by a mechanical or bioprosthetic conduit (pre-fabricated tubular vascular prosthesis with implanted aortic valve replacement) in annuloaortic ectasia (0-9%) (Fig. 97).

In some patients with dilatation of the aortic root, a replacement of the root while preserving the native aortic valve (with its reconstruction) is possible. The advantages of this method are: no need for anticoagulant drug regimen, improved hemodynamics (better blood flow through the native valve), lower risk of endocarditis as compared to mechanical valve replacement, and also low probability of thromboembolic complications (e.g. risk of cerebrovascular accident). Adversely, inadequate reconstruction of the native valve increases the risk of its failure.

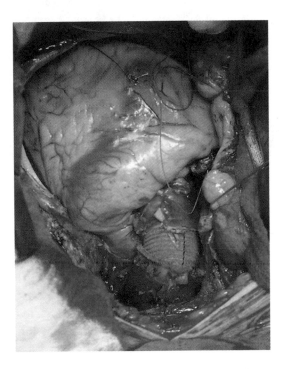

Fig. 96 A _ Perioperative image: isolated supracoronary replacement of the ascending aorta with a tubular vascular graft (Kolesar, 2008).

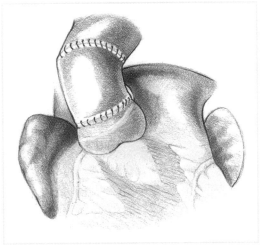

Fig. 96 B _ Isolated suprocoronary replacement of the ascending aorta with a tubular vascular garft (Valočik, 2013).

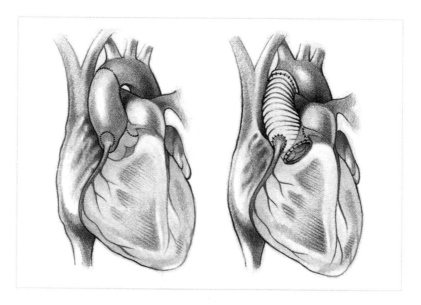

Fig. 97 _ Aortic root replacement by a mechanical or bioprosthetic conduit (prefabricated tubular vascular prosthesis with implanted aortic valve replacement) (Valočik, 2013).

In general, in can be said that elective results in this area, including results for large aneurysms, pose acceptable risk. Open surgical treatment is in this case preferred to disease management (pharmacological treatment), where dissection or ascending aortic aneurysm rupture may occur. For cases where both ascending aortic and aortic arch aneurysms are present, replacement of the ascending aorta and the aortic arch (partial, total) are indicated. This is a technically more demanding procedure, where the surgeon will require a bloodless operating field by the open aortic arch due to the reconstruction of the anastomoses of the epiaortic vessels and descending aorta. After establishing the extracorporeal circuit and inducing cardiac arrest by administering cardioplegic solution, it is necessary to temporarily cease cardiopulmonary bypass (circulatory arrest) and induce a controlled clinical death. It is known that the central nervous system and spinal cord are most sensitive to hypoxia and ischemia. Protection of these structures is therefore crucial during circulatory arrest. Extremely serious complications can include postoperative paraplegia or paraparesis due to spinal cord ischemia. The intercostal arteries from the lower region of the thoracic artery supply the spinal cord via segmental radicular arteries, which supply anterior spinal artery and two posterior spinal arteries. The most vulnerable is a region supplied from the large unpaired great anterior radiculomedullary artery, which was described in 1882 by Adamkiewicz (Svensson et al., 1994).

Its anatomical location is highly variable and is most often found originating in the region between Th5 and L3 (Minatoya et al., 2002).

There are a few surgical techniques and approaches for prolonging and detecting the "safe" duration of the ischemic interval. These include: local perfusion of the CNS and the spinal cord via right subclavian artery and intercostal arteries, systemic and local hypothermia, barbiturate-induced coma, drainage and pressure monitoring of cerebrospinal fluid, measurement of somatosensoric and motoric potentials of tibial nerve, etc. (Tab. 13).

The mortality of these elective procedures increases to 6-14%. It is logical that the percentage of neurological complication is also increased (10-20%). Open repair surgery of the descending aortic aneurysm is performed through a left posterolateral thoracotomy (Fig. 98). Mortality of the elective procedures in this localisation is 5-10%. Paraplegia prevails in rate of occurrence as a potential risk of neurological complications. With thoracoabdominal aneurysms (Fig. 99), the entire affected part of the descending aorta

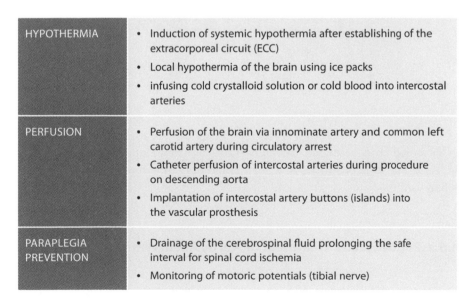

HYPOTHERMIA	• Induction of systemic hypothermia after establishing of the extracorporeal circuit (ECC) • Local hypothermia of the brain using ice packs • infusing cold crystalloid solution or cold blood into intercostal arteries
PERFUSION	• Perfusion of the brain via innominate artery and common left carotid artery during circulatory arrest • Catheter perfusion of intercostal arteries during procedure on descending aorta • Implantation of intercostal artery buttons (islands) into the vascular prosthesis
PARAPLEGIA PREVENTION	• Drainage of the cerebrospinal fluid prolonging the safe interval for spinal cord ischemia • Monitoring of motoric potentials (tibial nerve)

Tab. 13. _ Methods of CNS and spinal cord protection during systemic circulatory arrest (Cohn, 2011).

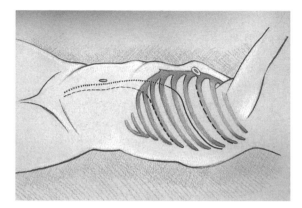

Fig. 98 _ Left posterolateral thoraco-phreno-laparotomy (Valočik, 2013).

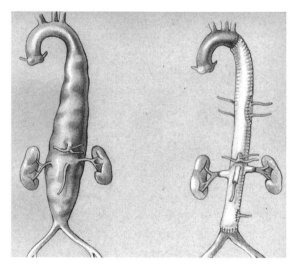

Fig. 99 _ Thoraco-abdominal aneurysm resection and its replacement with a prosthesis, including implantation of renal and intercostal arteries (Th7–L3) (Valočik, 2013).

is resected and replaced through thoraco-phreno-laparotomy. Mortality is 5-15%. These procedures are performed only at a few selected hospitals (Cohn, 2011).

3.6.2 Endovascular Treatment of Aortic Aneurysm

Endovascular treatment, also known as endovascular aortic repair (EVAR), is most commonly used for addressing aneurysms of the descending, thoracoabdominal and abdominal aorta. This is due to the lower risk of aneurysm rupture (and sudden death from subsequent exsanguination), and also due to elimination of peripheral embolisation risk. It is also possible to combine endovascular aortic repair with open surgery treatment. One such example is surgical debranching of epiaortic vessels of the aneurysmal aortic arch, after which in the second stage a stent-graft is implanted (self-expandable metal stent covered with synthetic material – dacron) into the ascending aorta with complete exclusion of the aortic arch (Fig. 100, 101). This hybrid approach is indicated for polymorbid patients, for whom extensive open surgery of the aortic arch (total aortic arch replacement) can be associated with high mortality and morbidity (Sabol et al., 2014). Aortic stent-grafts are contraindicated for anatomically unsuitable aneurysms, septic status, etc.

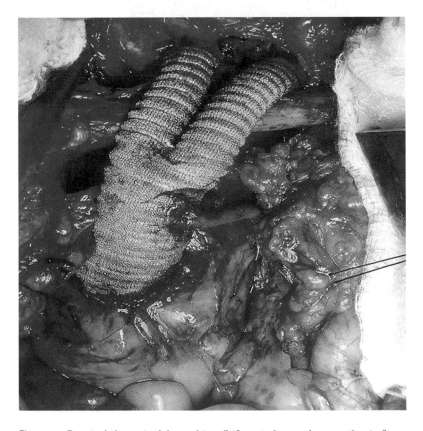

Fig. 100 _ Surgical thoracic debranching (bifurcated vascular prosthesis from the ascending aorta to innominate artery and left common carotid artery) (Sabol et al., 2014).

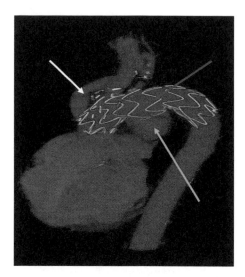

Fig. 101 _ After hybrid aortic arch treatment (same patient as in Fig. 100, CT scan): bifurcated vascular prosthesis (white arrow); stentgraft (red arrow); excluded aortic arch aneurysm (green arrow) (Sabol et al., 2014).

3.6.3 Pharmacologic treatment of Aortic Aneurysm

Conservative or pharmacological treatment is indicated for asymptomatic aneurysms that do not meet the indication criteria for open surgical or endovascular treatment. It is also indicated in high-risk polymorbid patients, for which the risk associated with surgery is disproportionately high. The treatment rather focuses in correcting the arterial hypertension (beta-blockers, antihypertensive drugs, etc.).

3.7 Conclusion

Aortic aneurysm is one of the most serious conditions affecting the vascular system. It is more prevalent than currently expected and diagnosed; however, it is also easily diagnosable and treatable. One year from initial diagnosis, the survival rate is 60% in observed patients . The survival rate five years from initial diagnosis is only 20%. Progressive enlargement of aneurysm diametre by more than 5-10mm per year or an onset of symptoms due to an obstruction of surrounding structures serves as a warning sign. Untreated aortic aneurysm patients with Marfan syndrome have an average life expectancy of 40 years; with Loyes-Dietz syndrome it is 10 years less.

The seriousness of this disease is exacerbated by minimal clinical symptoms. The main diagnostic methods are echocardiography (method of choice for ascending aortic aneurysm) and CT angiography. Elective aneurysm repair does not carry a very high risk; however, the risk significantly increases in surgery performed to address acute complications due to an aneurysm. Asymptomatic aneurysm of the ascending aorta is indicated for surgical intervention for a diametre greater than 55mm. In connective tissue disorders (Marfan syndrome, Ehlers-Danlos syndrome, Loyes-Dietz syndrome, etc.), surgery is indicated for a diametre of only 45mm. In congenital heart defects (Bicuspid aortic valve), a procedure on the ascending aorta is indicated when the aneurysm reaches a diametre equal to, or greater than 50mm (European Society of Cardiology Guidelines, 2012). Smaller asymptomatic aneurysms are periodically (two times a year) monitored (CT angiography). Symptomatic aneurysm, or its rupture, are indicated for urgent surgical intervention.

Dissection and Transection of the Aorta

4.1 Definition and classification of Aortic Dissection

Acute aortic dissection (AAD) is the most common fatal diagnosis. Global frequency of occurrence is 0.52–2.95/100,000 people, with additional occurrences of 2000 people per year in the United States. These statistical figures are not very exact, since many lethal cases go without acute aortic dissection diagnosis. Erbel et al. state that only in 15% of these cases an autopsy was performed to determine the cause of death (Erbel et al., 1989, 1993, 2001).

Rupture of the aorta with AAD has a mortality rate of 80% and in up-to 50% of cases patients die prior to hospital admission.

Systematically, acute aortic dissection can be categorised based on a few aspects. The two most widely accepted classification schemes are classification according to DeBakey and Stanford's classification (Fig. 102; Cohn, 2011).

According to localisation (Stanford classification):

- Type A: affects ascending aorta and/or aortic arch, alternatively including descending aorta;
- Type B: descending aorta or aortic arch (begins beyond brachiocephalic vessels).

According to localisation (DeBakey classification):

- DeBakey I: involves Ascending and Descending aorta (found in 60% of AAD cases) = Stanford A;
- DeBakey II: Ascending aorta is affected only (10-15% of AAD cases) = Stanford A;
- DeBakey III: Descending Aorta is affected only (25-30% of AAD cases) = Stanford B.

According to pathogenetic mechanisms:

- Classic aortic dissection;
- Intramural hematoma (IMH);
- Localised aortic dissection with excentric bulging;
- Disruption of the atherosclerotic plaque (penetrating aortic ulcer – PAU) with aortic dissection or rupture of the aorta;
- Traumatic or iatrogenic aortic dissection.

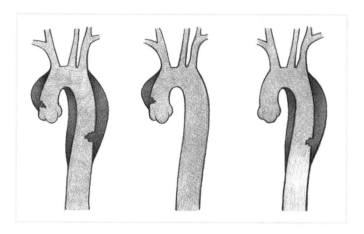

Fig. 102 _ Acute Aortic Dissection Classification (Valočik, 2013).

60 %	10 – 15 %	25 – 30 %
DeBakey I	DeBakey II	DeBakey III
Stanford A		Stanford B

According to the time period from dissection onset to the time of diagnosis:

- Acute Aortic Dissection (within 48 hours of AAD onset);
- Subacute Aortic Dissection (within 14 days of AAD onset);
- Chronic Aortic Dissection (more than 14 days from AAD onset).

4.2 Aortic Dissection Pathophysiology

Pathophysiological substrate of AAD is the formation of a tear (*entry intimal flap*) in the intima of aortic wall and subsequent entry of blood into the media layer of the aortic wall, caused by damage (most often due to hypertensive crisis) (Fig. 103).

The propagation of the aortic dissection is typically in antegrade manner; however, retrograde (opposite of the blood flow) propagation away from the initial intimal tear is not uncommon.

Pathophysiological algorithm of AAD origin:

1) Aortic wall tear;
2) Intramural aortic hematoma;
3) Pseudoaneurysm (rupture of the aortic wall);
4) Aortic dissection.

Dissection spread with antegrade manner can progress all the way under the bifurcation of the aorta; the dissected wall can rupture or re-canalise back to the intravascular (right) lumen (*double barrel aorta*). This lowers the pressure and tension on the dissected aortic wall and therefore decreases rupture risk.

A rupture causes bleeding into the preformed sinuses; the prognosis is dependent on rupture localisation.

Initial tear (entry) causes blood flow entry into the media layer of the aorta, as a result of which a false lumen is created. True and false lumens are separated from one another by intimal tissue (intimal flap).

Most AAD occurs from tears in the ascending aorta (65%). Primary tear of the aortic arch can be found in 10% of AAD cases. The descending aorta as a primary source of onset of AAD occurs in 20% of cases.

Distal blood flow through the false lumen can cause secondary tear in the intima layer (re-entry) In this case, blood from the false lumen can re-enter the physiological lumen of the aorta. A frequent cause of secondary tear is collagen and elastin degeneration of the media layer. However, in

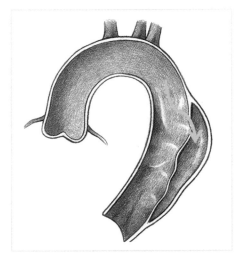

Fig. 103 _ AAD of the Descendeing Aorta with false lumen formation (yellow arrow) (Valočik, 2013).

13% of AAD cases, no evidence of an intima layer tear is observed. This is essentially the second pathogenetic principle of AAD origination, where primary rupture *vasa vasorum* occurs in the media layer of the aorta and an intramural hematoma (IMH) forms and only secondarily leads to the intima rupture and AAD. In light of the fact that the CT angiography or other imaging methods do not provide visualisation of the true and false lumen communication, it is difficult to diagnose AAD caused by IMH. The treatment of AAD caused by IMH does not differ from the treatment of AAD caused by intimal tear (Elefteriades, 2007). For more detailed information on aortic etiology refer to Chapter 3.3.

4.3 Aortic Dissection Etiology

Most commonly AAD is linked to arterial hypertension and many disorders of the connective tissue. Inflammation of the aorta results in aortic dissection rarely. Dissection can also be caused by a trauma; this case is referred to as aortic transection (see Chapter 4.8).

The potential causes of aortic dissection are closely linked or are identical to causes of aortic aneurysm (see Chapter 3.3).

1. Arterial Hypertension – Up to 80% of patients with AAD have a history of arterial hypertension. Most incidence of AAD occurs in patients between 50 and 70 years old. It occurs twice as often in men than women (Elefteriades, 2007).
2. Pregnancy – Approximately half of AAD cases in women under 40 years old occur during pregnancy (typically in the third trimester or shortly after delivery) (DePaepe et al., 1996).
3. Bicuspid Aortic Valve – This congenital defect is found in 7-14% of AAD cases. These patients present higher risk for AAD most often arising in the ascending aorta.
4. Tissue Disorders – Marfan Syndrome, Turner Syndrome and other tissue disorders (see Chapter 3.3)
5. Chest Trauma/Injury – Trauma which causes AAD is divided based on its etiology into two groups:
   a. Blunt chest trauma (car accident, falls),
   b. Iatrogenic damage during cardiac catheterisation, percutaneous intervention, introduction of intra-aortic balloon counterpulsation, cardiopulmonary resuscitation or general cardiac surgery.

Associated with the development of invasive diagnostic and therapeutic methods is the more frequent occurrence of iatrogenic and postcatheterisation dissections. Even more frequent is the occurrence of dissection after cardiac surgery; for example, after aortic valve replacement at the site of aorta cannulation or during intra-aortic balloon counterpulsation introduction. The site of dissection is based on the nature of these procedures. After cardiac surgery procedures, 69% of cases present Type A dissection with antegrade manner; after catheterisation, 87% of cases present Type B dissection with retrograde manner (Januzi et al., 2002; Kirklin, 2002).

6. Toxic damage to the Aorta – Presents less frequent cause of the dissection of the aortic wall. It can occur in cases of amphetamine, cocaine or nicotine abuse (Kirklin, 2012).

The most common causes of aortic dissection are presented in Table 14.

Anatomical aberrations / Congenital Defects	Bicuspid aortic valve
	Aortic coarctation
	Aberrant Right Subclavian artery
	Congenital aortic stenosis
	Hypoplastic aortic arch
Hereditary and Genetic Malformations (Syndromes)	Marfan Syndrome (FBN mutation)
	Ehlers-Danlos Syndrome - type IV (COL3A1 mutation)
	Loyes-Dietz Syndrome (TGFBR2 mutation)
	Turner Syndrome (45, X karyotype)
	Polycystic kidney disease
	Noonan Syndrome
Genetic Malformations (non-syndrome)	ACTA2
	MYH11
	TGFBR2
Cardiovascular Risk Factors	Arterial Hypertension
	Dyslipidemia
	Intramural Hematoma
	Aortic Aneurysm

Lifestyle Factors	Nicotine Abuse
	Cocaine Abuse
Inflammatory Diseases	Takayasu arteritis
	Giant cell arteritis
	Behcet's disease
	Ankylosing spondylitis

ACTA = smooth muscle- specific alpha actin; MYH11 = smooth muscle cell-specific myosin heavy chain 11; TGFBR = transrforming growth factor-beta receptor

Tab. 14 _ Most common causes of aortic dissection (Elefteriades, 2007).

4.4 Aortic Dissection Clinical Symptomatology

Symptoms of AAD can be divided into two groups. General symptoms (Tab. 15) are associated with the formation of an intimal disruption and its propagation. Approximately 96% of AAD patients report sudden intensive pain, which can be retrosternal radiating into the neck (in 73% of cases), antegrade (distal from the heart) radiating into the intrascapular area (in 53% of cases), or radiating into the epigastrium (in 30% of cases) (Cohn, 2011). The greater the arterial pressure, the greater the pain.

PAIN AND ITS LOCATION	• Intense, sudden onset, retrosternal • Radiating into the intrascapular area, neck and epigastrium; paravertebral and distally
NONSPECIFIC SYMPTOMS	• Cephalalgia • Tinnitus • Nausea etc.
BLEEDING	• Into the pericardium (pericardial effusion and resulting cardiac tamponade) • Into the pleural cavity (left hemothorax)

Tab. 15 _ General Clinical Symptoms of AAD (Cohn, 2011).

The main source of pain is intramural pressure on nerve endings in arterial adventitia of the aorta. In AAD patients with latent disease progression, the condition becomes known as a chronic aortic dissection after 14 days.

In instances when blood seeps into the ascending aorta adventitia, pericardial effusion can arise and result in a cardiac tamponade. Without immediate surgical (or pericardiocentesis) intervention, exitus or cardiogenic shock, accompanied by all its typical symptoms, can occur. Blood seeping or full bleeding of the aorta can occur in various levels of the aorta, depending on the location of the initial tear site, either into the pericardium, pleura, mediastinum, or retroperitoneum (Elefteriades, 2007).

Another group of clinical symptoms are of organ malperfusion. These can be didactically divided according to the affected anatomical levels of the aorta (Tab. 16).

4.5 Diagnostic modalities of Aortic Dissection

A basic, although often underestimated non-imaging diagnostic method, is medical histories and physical examination. In cases where a patient is in a stable, non-life threatening condition, review of the family history (for cardiac and vascular diseases) is performed.

In a personal anamnesis, the search focus is on the presence of arterial hypertension as one of the main causing factors of dissection. With appropriate questions, the intensity, initial onset, and propagation of pain are

| ASCENDING AORTA AND AORTIC ROOT | • Aortic heart valve disease (in 32% of ascending aorta AAD cases)
  – Cause A: Dilation of the valve annulus and central regurgitation (insufficient leaflet coaptation)
  – Cause B: Aortic root dissection disrupts leaflet attachments or valve commissures.
  – Cause C: Prolapse of an extensive intimal flap into the LVOT
• Involvement of coronary arteries – symptoms of acute myocardial infraction (in 1-2% of ascending aorta AAD cases)
• Pericardial bleeding – cardiac tamponade with cardiogenic shock symptoms |

AORTIC ARCH	• Involvement of innominate artery and left common carotid artery – neurological symptomatology • Syncope (in 7% of AAD cases) • Cerebrovascular accident (in 3-6% of AAD cases) • Paralysis, vision, and consciousness disorders, etc.
DESCENDING AND ABDOMINAL AORTA	• Disruption of Adamkiewicz artery can cause paraplegia as a result of impairment of distal intercostal arteries • Dissection progressing into celiac artery leads to hepatic failure symptoms • Involvement of mesenteric arteries can present as a sudden abdominal event and paralytic ileus • Dissection of renal arteries result in oliguria and renal failure

Tab. 16 _ Symptoms According to the Location of the Aortic Dissection.

assessed. During physical examination, emphasis is placed on a precise peripheral pulse palpation. An indicator of a suspected dissection is variable pulse quality. Auscultation of the heart and heart sounds can reveal aortic valve regurgitation (diastolic murmur in 2nd intercostal space with propagation to the heart apex) in cases of the ascending aorta or aortic root dissection.

Another group are imaging methods. The basic non-invasive imaging in suspected aortic dissection cases are transthoracic (TTE) and transesophageal (TEE) echocardiography. In cases when specific symptoms of AAD are present, but the clinical finding on TTE is negative, TEE is indicated. Together with TEE imaging confirming AAD, CT spiral angiography (CTA) is indicated due to its high accuracy (up to 95%) in confirming AAD, its progression, and extent (Figure 104). Similar sensitivity and specificity results of CTA are achievable with magnetic resonance angiography (MRA). An advantage of MRA is that it does not expose the patient to ionising radiation (Figure 105). Moreover, in patients with renal insufficiency, the MRA imaging does not require application of iodine contrast medium. Given the lower accessibility to this type of imaging technique, it is used mostly for hemodynamically stabile patients and patients with chronic aortic dissection. Classic aortography is reserved for patients in which endovascular treatment and coronarography are being considered. More detailed descriptions of imaging methods can be found in Chapter 2.

So far, laboratory tests play only a marginal role in the diagnosis of AAD. Often, elevated levels of C-reactive protein, D-dimer and leukocytosis can be detected. Establishing D-dimer levels is important in making a differential diagnosis between acute coronary syndrome (ACS) and AAD (Tab. 17). Tests administered to measure D-dimer levels in patients during hospital admission show D-dimer levels in patients with ACS are normal or only slightly elevated. In patients with AAD, these levels are elevated significantly and correlate directly to the extent of AAD (Dempfle et al., 2005).

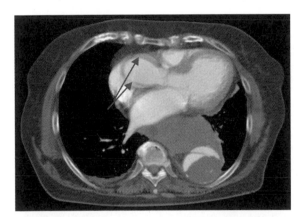

Fig. 104 _ CTA scan of aneurysmal dilation, aortic root and aortic dissection (see arrows) (Špak, 2014).

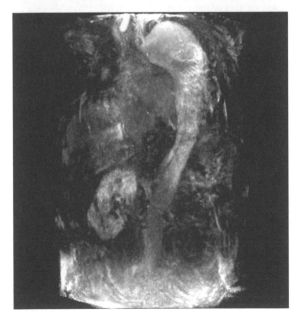

Fig. 105 _ MRI scan of descending aorta dissection (Špak, 2014).

	Elevated D-dimer	No D-dimer Elevation
Swelling of the extremities	– Deep vein thrombosis – Erysipelas – Osteomyelitis – Abscess – Trauma, malignancy	– Lymphedema – Cardiac insufficiency
Acute chest pain, dyspnea	– Acute aortic dissection – Pulmonary embolism – Aortic aneurysm – Pneumonia	– Acute myocardial infarction – Decompensated heart failure
Quick's test values decrease	– Consumptive coagulopathy – Acute liver failure	– lack of vitamin K – Synthesis malfunction in the liver – Losing coagulopathy

Tab. 17 _ Differential diagnostic use of D-dimer antigen in AAD (Dempfle, 2005)

4.6 Aortic Dissection Treatment

In cases of AAD, choice of treatment method depends on the location of the dissection site in the aorta. When referring to Type A (ascending aorta), the treatment method of choice is surgical intervention. For non-complicated Type B (descending aorta), including the abdominal aortic dissection, the preferred method is pharmacological treatment (Suzuki et al., 2003).

Risk of death due to AAD is highest within the first few hours from dissection formation and decreases afterwards. It is crucial to differentiate therapeutic strategy for treatment of AAD from the strategy for treatment of chronic aortic dissection.

Surgical approach and replacement of the affected section of the aorta does not differ in principle to surgical interventions for aortic aneurysm (see Chapter 3.6). Surgical access to the ascending aorta and aortic arch is gained via sternotomy. To access the descending aorta, an incision is made in the posterolateral part of the chest (posterolateral left thoracotomy within the third and fourth intercostal space. A fundamental difference between surgical procedures for aortic aneurysm and acute aortic dissection is the pronounced frailty of the aortic wall in aortic dissection cases. The aortic wall in AAD cases does not resemble a healthy aortic wall at all (wet toilet paper consistency). The most common causes for increased risk to the patient during surgical AAD intervention are a prolonged preoperative phase, older age, comorbidity (ischemic heart disease etc.), dissected aortic wall bleeding, cardiac tamponade, cardiogenic or hemorrhagic shock, myocardial infraction anamnesis, or renal failure (Cohn, 2011).

In principle, AAD surgeries are considered to be one of the most complex and technically challenging surgical procedures overall. The basis of surgical treatment is removal of the false aortic lumen entry. In most cases of aortic dissection, aortic replacement (supracoronary replacement, Bentall operation – Fig. 106) or reconstruction of the aorta and the aortic root (remodeling or re-implantation – Fig. 107) is performed. Importance is placed on visual assessment of the aortic arch (during circulatory arrest) in order to exclude or confirm finding of an additional intimal tear. If a tear is found in the aortic arch, it is also necessary to replace the affected section (partial arch replacement/total arch replacement) (Fig. 108).

In cases when intimal tears appear in the ascending aorta, aortic arch, as well as in the proximal section of the descending aorta, and therefore

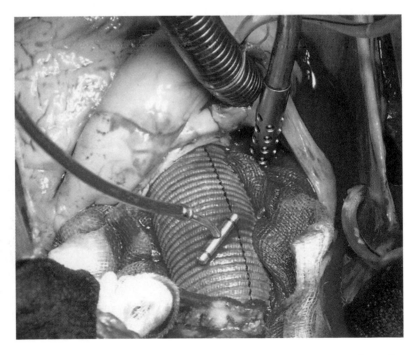

Fig. 106 _ Supracoronary replacement with a tubular vascular prosthesis for acute aortic dissection (Kolesar, 2008).

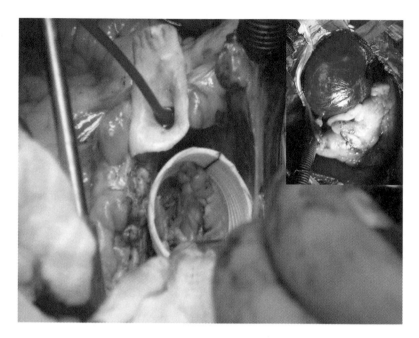

Fig. 107 _ Aortic valve reimplantation and ascending aorta (root) replacement using a Valsalva graft for an acute aortic dissection (upper right) (Kolesar, 2010).

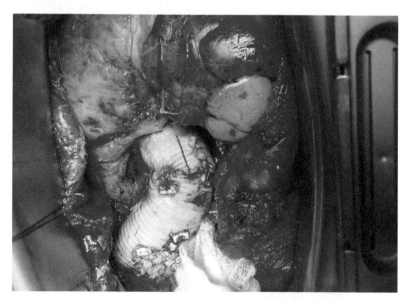

Fig. 108 _ A complex replacement of the aortic root, ascending aorta and aortic arch (total arch) – the *elephant trunk* created using a mechanical conduit and two tubular prosthesis (Kolesar, 2014).

surgical exclusion of all entries is impossible via a sternotomy called '*elephant trunk*' procedure can be considered; where after a complete replacement of the ascending aorta and aortic arch, a portion of the vascular prosthesis is left freely hanging in the proximal section of the descending aorta. The end of the prosthesis represents a "landing zone" for implantation of the stentgraft during the second phase of the surgery and for exclusion of the damaged aorta (Borst, 1983; Kolesár, 2015).

The surgical approach itself is modified according to a few criteria: actual surgical finding, overall condition of the patient, and surgeon skill and experience level.

Surgical treatment of Type B is currently not the method of choice and is rarely indicated. Indication criteria for surgical intervention for Type B are not defined with absolute certainty; however, the following criteria list presents some of those most widely accepted (Aposolakis, 2010):

1. Distal ischemia: visceral organs, kidneys, lower extremities;
2. Pain resistant to analgesic treatment;
3. Refractory hypertension not responding to pharmacological treatment;
4. Aortic rupture (risk of rupture);
5. Aortic expansion (increase in size);
6. Dissection in the area of aortic aneurysm;
7. Pseudoaneurysm;
8. Descending aorta dissection, including a section of the aortic arch;
9. Younger patient without comorbidities;
10. Marfan Syndrome;
11. Existing paraplegia (indication in the first few hours of onset);
12. Absence of endovascular treatment availability or suitability.

Due to the high surgical mortality and morbidity of acute and chronic descending aortic dissection, the preferred treatment method is endovascular repair, which consists of stent graft implantation intended to overlay the intimal tear and in doing so obturate the false lumen (Dake 1999; Ince, 2002; Fig. 109).

Endovascular treatment of Type B (indications) are:

1. Aortic rupture;
2. Refractory pain with no response to adequate analgesic treatment;
3. Organ and limb ischemia (malperfusion syndrome);
4. Peudoaneurysm or progressively enlarging diametre of the dissected aorta;
5. Uncontrollable hypertension.

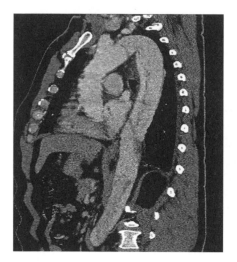 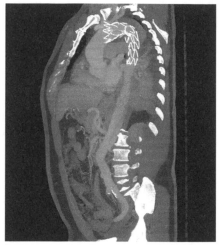

Fig. 109 _ CT scans of Type B with malperfusion syndrome complications (left image), and after endovascular stentgraft implantation (right image). The false lumen is partially thrombotic (left image) and completely excluded from circulation after treatment (right image) where a definite expansion of the true lumen can be observed.

In summary, use of the endovascular treatment of an aortic dissection Type B can be found in three main areas:

1) Stent graft implantation to achieve closure of the entry tear and blood flow normalisation into the true lumen, as well as relieving the false lumen thrombosis;
2) Stent implantation into the stenotic arteries to eliminate ischemia from the flow (static obstruction by false lumen);
3) Creation of a controlled re-entry in the intimal flap with decompression of the false lumen and improvement of peripheral blood circulation using percutaneous balloon fenestration (dynamic obstruction).

It is important to note that the endovascular treatment role for treatment of aortic dissection has not been yet fully established and concrete guidelines are not available.

Aortic dissection (apart from clinical symptoms) often manifests itself by a high degree of arterial hypertension.

The basic principles of pre-operative pharmacological treatment in patients with AAD are:

1. Correction of high blood pressure with the goal of reaching mean pressure of 60–70mmHg or lower (if tolerated by patient) and systolic pressure not exceeding 110mmHG;
2. Heart rate optimisation with target heart rate of 60-70 beats/minute;
3. Reduction of chamber ejection and reduction of power of impulse wave (anti-impulse therapy).

To reach the goals described above, antihypertensive drug therapy (mainly Nitroprusside Sodium) and beta blockers (e.g. esmolol, metoprolol) are ideal. Analgesic treatment is common, oftentimes requiring administration of opioid analgesics.

4.7. Conclusion

According to the Stanford classification (Type A), dissection without surgical intervention results in death in 60% of patients within 24 hours of onset. Within one week of onset, 20% of patients survive and only 5-10% survive past three months from onset. The main cause of mortality associated with aortic dissection is aortic rupture and bleeding out into preformed cavities (pericardium, pleura, retroperitoneum). Further causes of death may include acute coronary syndrome, cardiac failure due to acute massive aortic regurgitation, or less often occurring visceral or cerebral ischemia caused by obliteration of the arterial flow into the true lumen. Prognosis for patients with Type B acute dissection is not completely dire. In most cases, the false lumen is thrombotized. Less often the false lumen is endothelialized, forming a double barrel aorta. However, without treatment, this type of aorta has a tendency towards dilatation and aneurysm formation.

Aortic dissection can be classified based upon two main characteristics: according to the duration time into acute, subacute and chronic; and according to localisation based upon the often-used Stanford classification into Type A and Type B. Acute aortic dissection, especially of the ascending aorta, is a very serious condition. The only causal treatment is urgent intervention. For chronic aortic dissection found in the ascending aorta, surgical intervention is also urgently indicated; however, the procedure may be somewhat postponed. In cases without treatment complications, risk associated with surgery for Type B dissection is higher than risk associated with conservative treatment. Therefore, surgery is indicated only when life-threatening complications are present (malperfusion syndrome, bleeding). At this time, a surgical approach to treatment of Type B dissection is still rare, since a lower risk is associated with an endovascular treatment approach using a stent graft implant.

A patient with an AAD anamnesis of either type should be monitored and periodically examined by their cardiac care facility. Post aortic dissection surgery (or after endovascular intervention), the European Society of Cardiology recommends a series of ambulant exams after one, three, six and twelve months after, and once yearly thereafter (Vejvoda et al., 2005).

4.8. Aortic Transection

4.8.1. Definition and Clinical Symptomatology

Transection or traumatic aortic disruption is a common result of polytrauma. A typical site of damage location is the aortic isthmus. Clinical manifestation of post-trauma aortic rupture varies. The rupture presents itself by specific symptoms in less than 50% of cases. These symptoms in-

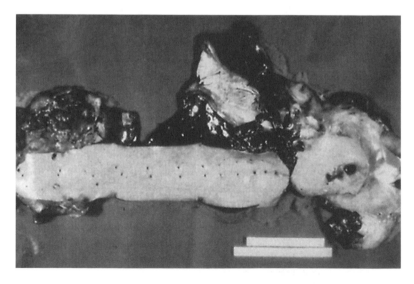

Fig. 110 _ Autoptic sample of a post-trauma aortic transection with exsanguination (Cohn, 2011).

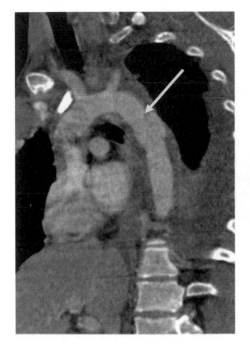

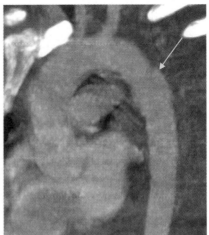

Fig. 111 _ CT scan of aortic transection post-trauma aortic transection (yellow arrow) in the area of the aortic isthmus (Špak, 2014).

Fig. 112 _ CT scan of a descending aorta pseudoaneurysm (arrow) with aortic transection after a trauma (Špak, 2014).

clude wheezing, back pain, hypertension in upper extremities, and paraparesis. Injury to the aorta is common in patients that suffered a polytrauma and the diagnosis is confirmed or ruled out only when aortic injury is suspected. The natural course of aortic transection depends on multiple factors. The most important of which is the speed of confirming the diagnosis. Autoptic sample analysis showed (Fig. 110) that 86% of patients die at the time of the accident and less than 10% of patients make it to the operating room. A certain portion of patients develop aortic pseudoaneurysm, caused by a weakened aortic wall at the site of disruption. In other words, the pseudoaneurysm sac is formed only by adventitia of the aorta (Fig. 111, 112).

4.8.2 Diagnostic Modalities of Aortic Transection

Examining the characteristics and mechanism of the injury is the basic first step in making the diagnostic assessment for aortic rupture. Considering that the first most common cause is a car accident at a speed of travel exceeding 50km/hr and absence of safety belts, it is important to search for injury signs on the ventral surface of the chest. Impressions of the steering wheel can be found upon visual examination of the chest. The second most common cause is a fall from more than three metres, where patients suffer multiple fractures of lower extremities and the pelvis (Cohn, 2011).

These mechanisms are generally referred to as deceleration injuries. The initial management of polytrauma patients consists of securing the airways and circulation. When an injury to the aorta is suspected, the next step is a classic anteroposterior chest X-ray. A widened mediastinal shadow, hemothorax, or hemodynamic instability are symptoms which warrant considering this diagnosis. The gold standard in diagnostic assessment is the spiral CT angiography with contrast medium (Fig. 111). Another diagnostic examination performed is the transesophageal echocardiography (TEE). This method allows for examination of the entire aorta except for the distal section of the ascending aorta and proximal section of the aortic arch. The main advantages of TEE are transportability and minimal strain on the already hemodynamically compromised patient. Its simultaneous use with exploratory laparo- or thoracotomy is irreplaceable. Classic aortography is currently utilised less frequently due to its time consuming, necessity of a highly skilled interventional radiologist team and increased risk of renal failure after administration of a large dose of contrast medium. Nuclear magnetic resonance imaging is usually not indicated for acute aortic injury.

4.8.3. Aortic Transection Treatment

Immediately after aortic transection diagnosis is confirmed, a hemodynamically stable patient is indicated for surgery or endovascular stent graft implantation. Patients with associated injuries requiring a laparotomy or craniotomy (intracranial bleeding) undergo a transection correction procedure only after life-threatening hemorrhaging is under control (i.e. during the second phase). However, if symptoms of continuous bleeding (or incipient rupture) caused by transection are observed, patients require an emergency procedure. Hemodynamically unstable patients must be taken

into the operating room immediately before the definitive diagnostic conclusion is reached.

Anti-impulse therapy, using beta blockers or antihypertensive drugs, is
necessary to be initiated prior to surgical or endovascular intervention.
This is done to achieve maximum decrease of tension and stress on the
aortic wall.

Similarly to aortic aneurysm or aortic dissection, the treatment of aortic transection involves three options: endovascular, surgical or conservative (pharmacological) treatment.

Even though the stent graft approach for treatment of aortic aneurysm
and dissection in the area of the descending aorta has, in comparison to
surgical treatment, substantiated advantages, its advantages for use with
aortic transection are not as definitive. The scientific literature does not of-
fer many extensive articles comparing these treatment options. More available are limited works or casuistry. The current spectrum of stent graft
sizes available includes sizes with larger diametres than that of descending
aorta. Stent grafts were originally developed for the treatment of aortic
aneurysm, not to address aortic transection. However, a simple and fast
bridging over of an unstable patient with the help of a deployed stentgraft
until they are in a stable condition associated with formation of chronic
pseudoaneurysm has clear advantages when compared to classic surgical
replacement of the affected section of the aorta in an unstable patient with
polytrauma.

Surgical access to the distal region of the aortic arch and upper section of the descending aorta is gained by left posterolateral thoracotomy
via the fourth intercostal space. There are two main surgical techniques
for the replacement of the affected section of the aorta. In the first case,
after clamps are placed on the aorta above the tear and distally to it, the
excluded section of the aorta is opened. A vascular prosthesis is implanted
as quickly as possible into the disrupted aorta (*"clamp and sew"* technique).
A disadvantage of this surgical technique is the high risk of paraplegia
when the ischemic period exceeds 30–40 minutes. The advantage is that this
is a simple, fast and causal technique with no need for heparinisation. In
the second case, which is more commonly seen at cardiac surgery centres,
partial extracorporeal circuit (EEC) is used (Fig. 113).

A principal component in this case is the perfusion of the lower half
of the body distally from the distal clamp on the aorta. Venous drainage
is achieved through the right lower pulmonary vein and arterial access is
secured either into the descending aorta under the distal clamp, or into the

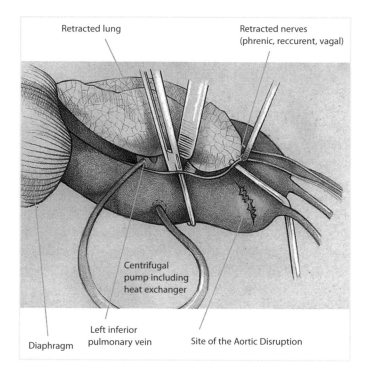

Fig. 113 _ Partial Bypass (with EEC) in a patient with aortic transection in the isthmus area (Valočik, 2013).

common femoral artery. After partial ECC is introduced (activated coagulation time (ACT) is kept in the range of 200– 300 seconds), the procedure continues as described above for the first case. This method offers a few advantages:

1. Lowers volume overload of the left ventricle after proximal clamp is placed;
2. Ensures perfusion of the lower body and de facto minimises paraplegia risk;
3. Allows more adequate treatment when encountered with hypotension and hypovolemia.

4.8.4 Conclusion

Aortic transection mortality of those patients who make it to the hospital is 7-65%. Mortality of the hemodynamically stable patients who undergo surgical or endovascular treatment is currently 0-20%. Risk of death for aortic transection patients for which serious injuries to other organs prevent appropriate aortic intervention is 55%. Based on data from scientific literature, risk of paraplegia is approximately 9.9%. However, when partial ECC is used, the risk is significantly reduced (Cohn, 2011).

More than 70% of injuries to the aorta are caused by a blunt trauma mechanism. Only a minority of patients are transported to the hospital and even then successful diagnostic assessment and adequate treatment are achieved in less than 50% of cases. The treatment is either surgical (replacement of the affected aorta section) or endovascular (stentgraft implant). A crucial component of the treatment is anti-impulse therapy, which lowers aortic wall pressure in the entire aorta and therefore lowers the overall rupture risk. Surgical intervention indication for hemodynamically unstable patients is urgent, whereas for patients in stabilised condition, endovascular treatment is preferred (Bortone et al., 2002). In cases where additional life-threatening injuries are present, corrective procedure for aortic transection is performed only after these are addressed.

List of Abbreviations

AA	Ascending Aorta
AAA	Abdominal Aortic Aneurysm
AAD	Acute Aortic Dissection
ACC	American College of Cardiology
ACC	*Arteria Carotis Communis*
ACT	Activated Clotting time
AD	Autosomal Dominant
AG	Aortography
AGS	Alagille Syndrome
AHA	American Heart Association
AIDS	Acquired Immune Deficiency Syndrome
ACS	Acute Coronary Syndrome
ANCAs	Anti-Neutrophil Cytoplasmic Antibodies
AR	Aortic Regurgitation
AS	Ankylosing Spondylitis
ASI	Aortic Size Index
ASS	*Arteria Subclavia Sinistra*
ATI l. sin.	*Arteria Thoracica Interna sinistra*
AVJ	Aortoventricular Junction
AVN	Atrioventricular Node
AVR	Aortic Valve Replacement
BAV	Bicuspid Aortic Valve
BS	Behcet's Syndrome
BSA	Body Surface Area
CCA	Congenital Contractural Arachnodactyly (Beals syndrome)
CNS	Central Nervous System
CoA	Coarctation of the Aorta
CRP	C-reactive Protein
CS	Cogan's Syndrome
CTA	Computed Tomography Angiography
ECC	Extracorporeal Circuit
EDS	Ehlers-Danlos syndrome
EF	Ejection Fraction
ESC	European Society of Cardiology
ESR	Erythrocyte Sedimentation Rate
EVAR	Endovascular Aortic Repair
FDG-PET	Positron Emission Tomography (with Fluorodeoxyglucose F-18)
GCA	Giant cell arteritis
GenTAC	National Registry of Genetically Triggered Thoracic Aortic Aneurysms and Cardiovascular Conditions
GIT	Gastrointestinal tract
HIV	Human Immunodeficiency Virus
HLA	Human Leukocyte Antigen
CHSsy	Churg–Strauss Syndrome
IABC (IABK)	Intra-aortic Balloon Counterpulsation
IBD	Inflammatory Bowel Disease
ICA	Intercostal Arteries

Ig A, M, E	Immunoglobulin A, M and E
IMH	Intramural Haematoma of the Aorta
IRAD	International Registry of Acute Aortic Dissections
IRF	Idiopathic retroperitoneal fibrosis
IVUS	Intravascular ultrasound
KFS	Klippel-Feil Syndrome
KS	Klinefert Syndrome
LDS	Loeys-Dietz Syndrome
LV	Left Ventricle
LTBP	Latent TGF-beta Binding Protein
LVOT	Left Ventricular Outflow Tract
MFS	Marfan syndrome
MMPs	Matrix Metalloproteinases
MR	Mitral Regurgitation
MRI	Magnetic Resonance Imaging
MRSA	*Methicillin-Resistant Staphylococcus Aureus*
MVR	Mitral Valve Replacement
NS	Noonan Syndrome
OI	*Osteogenesis Imperfecta*
PAU	Penetrating Atherosclerotic Ulcer
PET	Positron Emission Tomography
PET–CT	Positron Emission Tomography with CT Scan
PET–MRI	Positron Emission Tomography with MRI
PKD	Polycystic Kidney Disease
PXE	*Pseudoxanthoma Elasticum*
ReA	Reiter syndrome
RP	Relapsing Polychondritis
RTG	X-Ray
HR	Heart Rate
SGS	Shprintzen-Goldberg Syndrome
SLE	Systemic *lupus erythematodes*
STJ	Sinotubular junction
TA	Takayasu's Arteritis
TAAA	Thoraco-abdominal Aortic Aneurysm
TAV	Tricuspid Aortic Valve
TBC	*truncus brachiocephalicus (arteria anonyma)*
TEE	Transesophageal echocardiography
TEVAR	Thoracic Endovascular Aortic Repair
TGF-β	Transforming Growth Factor Beta
TIMPs	Endogenous Tissue Inhibitors of Metalloproteinases
TS	Turner Syndrome
TTE	Transthoracic Echocardiography
WAS	Wiskott–Aldrich Syndrome

6.

References

Aalberts, J. J., Van Den Berg, M. P., Bergman, J. E., et al. 2008. The many faces of aggressive aortic pathology: Loeys-Dietz syndrome. Neth Heart J, 2008, 9, p. 299-304.

Adeola, T., Adeleye, O., Potts, J. L., et al. 2001. Thoracic aortic dissection in a patient with autosomal dominant polycystic kidney disease. J Natl Med Assoc, 2001, 7-8, p. 282-287.

Agozzino, L., Ferraraccio, F., Esposito, S., et al. 2002. Medial degeneration does not involve uniformly the whole ascending aorta: morphological, biochemical and clinical correlations. Eur J Cardiothorac Surg, 2002, 4, p. 675-682.

Aksglaede, L., Link, K., Giwercman, A., et al. 2013. 47, XXY Klinefelter syndrome: clinical characteristics and age-specific recommendations for medical management. Am J Med Genet C Semin Med Genet, 2013, 1, p. 55-63.

Ahmed, W., Ahmad, Z. 2005. Takayasu's Arteritis: A Case Report With Global Arterial Involvement. RMJ, 2005, 1, p. 43-45.

Albornoz, G., Coady, M. A., Roberts, M., et al. 2006. Familial thoracic aortic aneurysms and dissections–incidence, modes of inheritance, and phenotypic patterns. Ann Thorac Surg, 2006, 4, p. 1400-1405.

Albright, A. L., Pollack, I. 2007. Principles and Practice of Pediatric Neurosurgery. New York: Thieme, 2007. 1296 p.

Aldrich, R. A., Steinberg, A. G., Campbell, D. C. 1954. Pedigree demonstrating a sex-linked recessive condition characterized by draining ears, eczematoid dermatitis and bloody diarrhea. Pediatrics, 1954, 2, p. 133-139.

Apostolakis, E., Baikoussis, N., Georgiopoulos, M., et al. 2010. Acute Type – B Aortic Dissection: The Treatment Strategy. Hellenic J Cardiol, 2010, 51, p. 338 – 347.

Bardakci, H., Kervan, U., Boysan, F., et al. 2007. Aortic arch aneurysm, pseudocoarctation, and coronary artery disease in a patient with Behcet's syndrome. Tex Heart Inst J, 2007, 3, p. 363-365.

Bentall, H., De Bono, A. 1968. A technique for complete replacement of the ascending aorta. Thorax, 1968, 4, p. 338-339.

Bojar, R. M., Turner, M. T., Valdez, S., et al. 1998. Homograft repair of a tuberculous pseudoaneurysm of the ascending aorta. Chest, 1998, 6, p. 1774-1776.

Bonser, R. S., Pagano, D., Lewis, M. E., et al. 2000. Clinical and patho-anatomical factors affecting expansion of thoracic aortic aneurysms. Heart, 2000, 3, p. 277-283.

Borovanský, E. 1979. Sústavná anatómia človeka I., II. Martin: Osveta, 1979. 962 p.

Borst, H.G., Walterbusch, G., Schaps, D. 1983. Extensive aortic replacement using "elephant trunk" prosthesis. Thorac Cardiovasc Surg, 1983, 1, p. 37-40.

Bortone, A. S., Schena, S., D'agostino, D., et al. 2002. Immediate versus delayed endovascular treatment of post-traumatic aortic pseudoaneurysms and type B dissections: retrospective analysis and premises to the upcoming European trial. Circulation, 2002, 12 Suppl 1, p. I234-240.

Bossone, E., Rampoldi, V., Nienaber, C. A., et al. 2002. Usefulness of pulse deficit to predict in-hospital complications and mortality in patients with acute type A aortic dissection. Am J Cardiol, 2002, 7, p. 851-855.

Brahan, R. B., Kahler, R. C. 1990. Clostridium septicum as a cause of pericarditis and mycotic aneurysm. J Clin Microbiol, 1990, 10, p. 2377-2378.

Bulvas, M., Sommerová, Z., Votava, J. 2003. Endovaskulární léčba aortální disekce. Cor Vasa, 2003, 3, p. 152-155.

Calvo-Romero, J. M. 2003. Giant cell arteritis. Postgrad Med J, 2003, 935, p. 511-515.

Chan, F. Y., Crawford, E. S., Coselli, J. S., et al. 1989. In situ prosthetic graft replacement for mycotic aneurysm of the aorta. Ann Thorac Surg, 1989, 2, p. 193-203.

Chang, W. L., Huang, C. M., Yang, Y. H., et al. 2004. Aortic aneurysm in systemic lupus erythematosus. J Microbiol Immunol Infect, 2004, 5, p. 310-312.

Chassaing, N., Martin, L., Calvas, P., et al. 2005. Pseudoxanthoma elasticum: a clinical, pathophysiological and genetic update including 11 novel ABCC6 mutations. J Med Genet, 2005, 12, p. 881-892.

Chau, E. M., Wang, E., Chiu, C. S., et al. 2006. Non-infectious aortitis: an important cause of severe aortic regurgitation. Asian Cardiovasc Thorac Ann, 2006, 3, p. 177-182.

Chello, M., Tamburrini, S., Mastroroberto, P., et al. 2002. Pseudoaneurysm of the thoracic aorta in patients with human immunodeficiency virus infection. Eur J Cardiothorac Surg, 2002, 3, p. 454-456.

Chen, L., Wang, X., Carter, S. A., et al. 2006. A single nucleotide polymorphism in the matrix metalloproteinase 9 gene (-8202A/G) is associated with thoracic aortic aneurysms and thoracic aortic dissection. J Thorac Cardiovasc Surg, 2006, 5, p. 1045-1052.

Chňupa, P. 2002. Odporúčania pre ECHOKG vyšetrenia pri ochoreniach aorty. Cardiol, 2002, 1, p. 215-216.

Chockalingam, A., Gnanavelu, G., Alagesan, R. 2004. Massive aortic aneurysm presenting as chest wall swelling. Heart, 2004, 3, p. 292.

Chowdhary, V. R., Crowson, C. S., Liang, K. P., et al. 2009. Cardiovascular risk factors and acute-phase response in idiopathic ascending aortitis: a case control study. Arthritis Res Ther, 2009, 1, p. R29.

Coady, M. A., Davies, R. R., Roberts, M., et al. 1999a. Familial patterns of thoracic aortic aneurysms. Arch Surg, 1999a, 4, p. 361-367.

Coady, M. A., Rizzo, J. A., Hammond, G. L., et al. 1999b. Surgical intervention criteria for thoracic aortic aneurysms: a study of growth rates and complications. Ann Thorac Surg, 1999b, 6, p. 1922-1926; discussion 1953-1928.

Cohn, E. 2011. Cardiac Surgery in the Adult, Fourth Edition. Boston: McGraw-Hill Professional, 2011. 1472 p.

Cochrane, A. D., Tatoulis, J. 1991. Cogan's syndrome with aortitis, aortic regurgitation, and aortic arch vessel stenoses. Ann Thorac Surg, 1991, 5, p. 1166-1167.

Černý, J., Němec, P., Ničovský, J., et al. 1997. Chirurgická léčba akutních stavů postihujících hrudní aortu. Cor Vasa, 1997, 2, p. 93-95.

Češka, R. 2010. Interna. Praha: Triton, 2010. 876 p.

Dake, M.D,, Kato, N., Mitchell, R.S,, et al. 1999. Endovascular stent-graft placement for the treatment of acute aortic dissection. N Engl J Med, 1999, 20, p. 1546-1552.

Davies, R. R., Gallo, A., Coady, M. A., et al. 2006. Novel measurement of relative aortic size predicts rupture of thoracic aortic aneurysms. Ann Thorac Surg, 2006, 1, p. 169-177.

Davies, R. R., Kaple, R. K., Mandapati, D., et al. 2007. Natural history of ascending aortic aneurysms in the setting of an unreplaced bicuspid aortic valve. Ann Thorac Surg, 2007, 4, p. 1338-1344.

Defendi, G.L., 2013. [on line]. Genetics of Ehlers-Danlos Syndrome. In: Medscape [citované 12. December 2014].

De Paepe, A., Devereux, R. B., Dietz, H. C., et al. 1996. Revised diagnostic criteria for the Marfan syndrome. Am J Med Genet, 1996, 4, p. 417-426.

Dean, J. C. 2007. Marfan syndrome: clinical diagnosis and management. Eur J Hum Genet, 2007, 7, p. 724-733.

Debakey, M. E., Henly, W. S., Cooley, D. A., et al. 1965. Surgical Management of Dissecting Aneurysms of the Aorta. J Thorac Cardiovasc Surg, 1965, p. 130-149.

Defendi, G.L., 2013. [online]. Genetics of Ehlers-Danlos Syndrome. In: Medscape [citované 12. December 2014]. < http://emedicine.medscape.com/article/943567-overview- >

Dempfe, C.E. 2005. Bestimmung des D-Dimer-Antigens in der klinischen Routine. Dtsch Arztebl, 2005, 7, p. A-428, B-361, C-336

Dib, C., Moustafa, S. E., Mookadam, M., et al. 2006. Surgical treatment of the cardiac manifestations of relapsing polychondritis: overview of 33 patients identified through literature review and the Mayo Clinic records. Mayo Clin Proc, 2006, 6, p. 772-776.

Dominik, J. 1998. Kardiochirurgie. Praha: Grada, 1998. 216 p.

Eagle, K. A., Isselbacher, E. M., Desanctis, R. W. 2002. Cocaine related aortic dissection in perspective. Circulation, 2002, 13, p. 1529-1530.

Elefteriades, J. 2007. Acute Aortic Disease (Fundamental and Clinical Cardiology). Yale: CRC Press, 2007. 400 p.

Elefteriades, J. A. 2002. Natural history of thoracic aortic aneurysms: indications for surgery, and surgical versus nonsurgical risks. Ann Thorac Surg, 2002, 5, p. S1877-1880; discussion S1892-1878.

Erbel, R., Alfonso, F., Boileau, C., et al. 2001. Diagnosis and management of aortic dissection. Eur Heart J, 2001, 18, p. 1642-1681.

Erbel, R., Engberding, R., Daniel, W., et al. 1989. Echocardiography in diagnosis of aortic dissection. Lancet, 1989, 8636, p. 457-461.

Erbel, R., Oelert, H., Meyer, J., et al. 1993. Effect of medical and surgical therapy on aortic dissection evaluated by transesophageal echocardiography. Implications for prognosis and therapy. The European Cooperative Study Group on Echocardiography. Circulation, 1993, 5, p. 1604-1615.

Erbel, R., Aboyans, V., Boileau, C., et al. 2014. 2014 ESC Guidelines on the diagnosis and treatment of aortic diseases: Document covering acute and chronic aortic diseases of the thoracic and abdominal aorta of the adultThe Task Force for the Diagnosis and Treatment of Aortic Diseases of the European Society of Cardiology (ESC). Eur Heart J, 2014, 41, p. 2873-2926.

Eskola, M. J., Niemela, K. O., Kuusinen, P. R., et al. 2002. Coronary artery dissection, combined aortic valve replacement and coronary bypass grafting in osteogenesis imperfecta. Interact Cardiovasc Thorac Surg, 2002, 2, p. 83-85.

Etz, C. D., Zoli, S., Brenner, R., et al. 2010. When to operate on the bicuspid valve patient with a modestly dilated ascending aorta. Ann Thorac Surg, 2010, 6, p. 1884-1890; discussion 1891-1882.

Farmakis, D., Vesleme, V., Papadogianni, A., et al. 2004. Aneurysmatic dilatation of ascending aorta in a patient with beta-thalassemia and a pseudoxanthoma elasticum-like syndrome. Ann Hematol, 2004, 9, p. 596-599.

Fenske, N.A., 2013. [on line]. Pseudoxanthoma Elasticum. In Medscape [citované 12. December 2014]. < http://emedicine.medscape.com/article/1074713-overview- >

Finkbohner, R., Johnston, D., Crawford, E. S., et al. 1995. Marfan syndrome. Long-term survival and complications after aortic aneurysm repair. Circulation, 1995, 3, p. 728-733.

Florian, M., Gebauerová, M., Marek, T., et al. 2001. Disekce aorty v těhotenství. Cor vasa, 2001, 10, p. 521-524.

Fuster, V., Halperin, J. L. 1994. Aortic dissection: a medical perspective. J Card Surg, 1994, 6, p. 713-728.

Gelsomino, S., Morocutti, G., Frassani, R., et al. 2003. Long-term results of Bentall composite aortic root replacement for ascending aortic aneurysms and dissections. Chest, 2003, 3, p. 984-988.

Gelsomino, S., Romagnoli, S., Gori, F., et al. 2005. Annuloaortic ectasia and giant cell arteritis. Ann Thorac Surg, 2005, 1, p. 101-105.

Goričan, K., Vařejka, P., Bělohlávek, J., et al. 1998. Echokardiografická diagnóza disekce aorty. Cor Vasa, 1998, 4, p. 195-200.

Gotway, M. B., Dawn, S. K. 2003. Thoracic aorta imaging with multisclice CT. Radiol Clin North Am, 2003, 3, p. 521-543.

Grasland, A., Pouchot, J., Hachulla, E., et al. 2004. Typical and atypical Cogan's syndrome: 32 cases and review of the literature. Rheumatology (Oxford), 2004, 8, p. 1007-1015.

Greally, M. T., Carey, J. C., Milewicz, D. M., et al. 1998. Shprintzen-Goldberg syndrome: a clinical analysis. Am J Med Genet, 1998, 3, p. 202-212.

Grocký, M., Babčák, M., Frajt, J., et al. 2001. Atypický prípad disekcie aorty. Cardiol, 2001, 2, p. 91-97.

Grocký, M., Viňanská, D., Pohly, M., et al. 2000. Chronická disekcia aorty. Cardiol, 2000, 2, p. 79-86.

Gupta, P. A., Putnam, E. A., Carmical, S. G., et al. 2002. Ten novel FBN2 mutations in congenital contractural arachnodactyly: delineation of the molecular pathogenesis and clinical phenotype. Hum Mutat, 2002, 1, p. 39-48.

Gupta, P. A., Wallis, D. D., Chin, T. O., et al. 2004. FBN2 mutation associated with manifestations of Marfan syndrome and congenital contractural arachnodactyly. J Med Genet, 2004, 5, p. e56.

Hagan, P. G., Nienaber, C. A., Isselbacher, E. M., et al. 2000. The International Registry of Acute Aortic Dissection (IRAD): new insights into an old disease. Jama, 2000, 7, p. 897-903.

Hamano, K., Minami, Y., Fujimura, Y., et al. 1994. Emergency operation for thoracic aortic aneurysm caused by the Ehlers-Danlos syndrome. Ann Thorac Surg, 1994, 4, p. 1180-1182.

Hannallah, R. S. 1991. Selection of patients for paediatric ambulatory surgery. Can J Anaesth, 1991, 7, p. 887-890.

Hasham, S. N., Willing, M. C., Guo, D. C., et al. 2003. Mapping a locus for familial thoracic aortic aneurysms and dissections (TAAD2) to 3p24-25. Circulation, 2003, 25, p. 3184-3190.

Hata, M., Shiono, M., Inoue, T., et al. 2003. Optimal treatment of type B acute aortic dissection: long-term medical follow-up results. Ann Thorac Surg, 2003, 6, p. 1781-1784.

Heikkinen, M. A., Dake, M. D., Alsac, J. M., et al. 2005. Multiple HIV-related aneurysms: open and endovascular treatment. J Endovasc Ther, 2005, 3, p. 405-410.

Hernandez, C., 2013 [on line]. Dermatologic Manifestations of Churg-Strauss Syndrome (Allergic Granulomatosis). In: Medscape [citované 12. December 2014]. < http://emedicine.medscape.com/article/1083013-overview-Churg-straus >

Heřman, M., Bučil, J. 2001. Magnetická rezonance: kontraindikace a kardiologické indikace. Kapitoly z kardiologie, 2001, 2, p. 46-50.

Hetzer, R., Delmo Walter, E. M., Meyer, R., et al. 2008. Isolated giant aortic aneurysm in an infant: Ehlers-Danlos syndrome type IV. Ann Thorac Surg, 2008, 2, p. 632-634.

Hiratzka, L. F., Bakris, G. L., Beckman, J. A., et al. 2010. 2010 ACCF/AHA/AATS/ACR/ ASA/SCA/SCAI/SIR/STS/SVM guidelines for the diagnosis and management of patients with Thoracic Aortic Disease: a report of the American College of Cardiology Foundation/American Heart Association Task Force on Practice Guidelines, American Association for Thoracic Surgery, American College of Radiology, American Stroke Association, Society of Cardiovascular Anesthesiologists, Society for Cardiovascular Angiography and Interventions, Society of Interventional Radiology, Society of Thoracic Surgeons, and Society for Vascular Medicine. Circulation, 2010, 13, p. e266-369.

Hsue, P. Y., Salinas, C. L., Bolger, A. F., et al. 2002. Acute aortic dissection related to crack cocaine. Circulation, 2002, 13, p. 1592-1595.

Ikonomidis, J. S., Spinale, F. G. 2004. Invited Commentary. Ann Thorac Surg, 2004, 78, p. 2106 – 11.

Ince, H., Nienaber, C. A. 2002. The concept of interventional therapy in acute aortic syndrome. J Card Surg, 2002, 2, p. 135-142.

Isselbacher, E. M., Cigarroa, J. E., Eagle, K. A. 1994. Cardiac tamponade complicating proximal aortic dissection. Is pericardiocentesis harmful? Circulation, 1994, 5, p. 2375-2378.

Januzzi, J. L., Sabatine, M. S., Eagle, K. A., et al. 2002. Iatrogenic aortic dissection. Am J Cardiol, 2002, 5, p. 623-626.

Johansen, K., Devin, J. 1983. Mycotic aortic aneurysms. A reappraisal. Arch Surg, 1983, 5, p. 583-588.

Kainulainen, K., Palotie, L., Savolainen, A., et al. 1990. The Marfan syndrome gene is localized. Duodecim, 1990, 21, p. 1453-1455.

Kamath, B. M., Spinner, N. B., Emerick, K. M., et al. 2004. Vascular anomalies in Alagille syndrome: a significant cause of morbidity and mortality. Circulation, 2004, 11, p. 1354-1358.

Kamp, T. J., Goldschmidt-Clermont, P. J., Brinker, J. A., et al. 1994. Myocardial infarction, aortic dissection, and thrombolytic therapy. Am Heart J, 1994, 6 Pt 1, p. 1234-1237.

Kanáliková, K., Jelok, I., Fischer, V., et al. 1998. Artériová hypertenzia a disekcia aorty. Cardiol, 1998, 2, p. 81-84.

Karakurt, C., Kocak, G., Selimoglu, A., et al. 2007. Aortic aneurysm: a rare complication of ulcerative colitis. Anadolu Kardiyol Derg, 2007, 4, p. 461-462.

Karnis, M. F., Zimon, A. E., Lalwani, S. I., et al. 2003. Risk of death in pregnancy achieved through oocyte donation in patients with Turner syndrome: a national survey. Fertil Steril, 2003, 3, p. 498-501.

Kawano, Y., Tamura, A., Kadota, J. 2006. Klippel-Feil syndrome accompanied by an aneurysm of the non-coronary sinus of Valsalva. Intern Med, 2006, 20, p. 1191-1192.

Khau Van Kien, P., Mathieu, F., Zhu, L., et al. 2005. Mapping of familial thoracic aortic aneurysm/dissection with patent ductus arteriosus to 16p12.2-p13.13. Circulation, 2005, 2, p. 200-206.

Khawaja, O. M., Reed, J. T., Shaefi, S., et al. 2009. Crisis resource management of the airway in a patient with Klippel-Feil syndrome, congenital deafness, and aortic dissection. Anesth Analg, 2009, 4, p. 1220-1225.

Kirklin, J. W., Barratt-Boyes, et al. 2012. Cardiac Surgery. 4th edition. Churchill Livingstone Inc. Saunders, 2012. 2256 p.

Kirsch, E. W., Radu, N. C., Allaire, E., et al. 2006. Pathobiology of idiopathic ascending aortic aneurysms. Asian Cardiovasc Thorac Ann, 2006, 3, p. 254-260.

Klásková, E., Zapletalová, A., Sobek, D., et al. 2010. Postižení kardiovaskulárního systému u žen s Turnerovým syndromem, kardiovaskulární rizika spojená s těhotenstvím. Prakt Gyn, 2010, 3, p. 142-146.

Klompas, M. 2002. Does this patient have an acute thoracic aortic dissection? Jama, 2002, 17, p. 2262-2272.

Kouchoukos, N.T., Blackstone, E.H., Hanley, F.L., et al. 2012. Cardiac Kirklin/Barratt-Boyes Cardiac Surgery. Philadelphia: Saunders, 2012. 2256 p.

Koullias, G. J., Ravichandran, P., Korkolis, D. P., et al. 2004. Increased tissue microarray matrix metalloproteinase expression favours proteolysis in thoracic aortic aneurysms and dissections. Ann Thorac Surg, 2004, 6, p. 2106-2110; discussion 2110-2101.

Křupka, B., Hlobilková, A., Galuszka, J., et al. 2002. Disekce aorty – jedna z méně častých příčin ischemického iktu, Kasuistika a přehled literatury. Cor Vasa, 2002, 3, p. 143-146.

Kvitting, J. P., Ebbers, T., Wigstrom, L., et al. 2004. Flow patterns in the aortic root and the aorta studied with time-resolved, 3-dimensional, phase-contrast magnetic resonance imaging: implications for aortic valve-sparing surgery. J Thorac Cardiovasc Surg, 2004, 6, p. 1602-1607.

Lambrechts, D., Casselman, F., Schroeyers, P., et al. 2003. Endovascular treatment of the descending thoracic aorta. Eur J Vasc Endovasc Surg, 2003, 4, p. 437-444.

Lee, Y. C., Wilson, C. J., Winship, I. M., et al. 2000. Marfanoid habitus, dysmorphic features, and web neck. South Med J, 2000, 12, p. 1197-1200.

Le Gloan, L., Pichon, O., Isidor, B., et al. 2008. A 8.26Mb deletion in 6q16 and a 4.95Mb deletion in 20p12 including JAG1 and BMP2 in a patient with Alagille syndrome and Wolff-Parkinson-White syndrome. Eur J Med Genet, 2008, 6, p. 651-657.

Lemaire, S. A., Wang, X., Wilks, J. A., et al. 2005. Matrix metalloproteinases in ascending aortic aneurysms: bicuspid versus trileaflet aortic valves. J Surg Res, 2005, 1, p. 40-48.

Lansac, E., Di Centa, I., Raoux, F., et al. 2009. An expansible aortic ring for a physiological approach to conservative aortic valve surgery. J Thorac Cardiovasc Surg., 2009, 3, p. 718-724.

Lin, C. Y., Hong, G. J., Lee, K. C., et al. 2003. Successful treatment of Salmonella mycotic aneurysm of the descending thoracic aorta. Eur J Cardiothorac Surg, 2003, 2, p. 320-322.

Long, R., Guzman, R., Greenberg, H., et al. 1999. Tuberculous mycotic aneurysm of the aorta: review of published medical and surgical experience. Chest, 1999, 2, p. 522-531.

Longo, D., Fauci, A., Kasper, D. 2011. Harrison's Principles of Internal Medicine. Boston: McGraw-Hill Professional, 2011. 4012 p.

Lozada, C.J., 2014 [on line]. Reactive Arthritis. In: Medscape [citované 12. December 2014]. < http://emedicine.medscape.com/article/331347-overview-reactive >

Macedo, T. A., Stanson, A. W., Oderich, G. S., et al. 2004. Infected aortic aneurysms: imaging findings. Radiology, 2004, 1, p. 250-257.

Markl, M., Draney, M. T., Miller, D. C., et al. 2005. Time-resolved three-dimensional magnetic resonance velocity mapping of aortic flow in healthy volunteers and patients after valve-sparing aortic root replacement. J Thorac Cardiovasc Surg, 2005, 2, p. 456-463.

Matouk, C. C., Hanbidge, A., Mandell, D. M., et al. 2011. Osteogenesis imperfecta, multiple intra-abdominal arterial dissections and a ruptured dissecting-type intracranial aneurysm. Interv Neuroradiol, 2011, 3, p. 371-375.

Matura, L. A., Ho, V. B., Rosing, D. R., et al. 2007. Aortic dilatation and dissection in Turner syndrome. Circulation, 2007, 15, p. 1663-1670.

Mehta, R. H., Manfredini, R., Hassan, F., et al. 2002a. Chronobiological patterns of acute aortic dissection. Circulation, 2002a, 9, p. 1110-1115.

Mehta, R. H., Suzuki, T., Hagan, P. G., et al. 2002b. Predicting death in patients with acute type a aortic dissection. Circulation, 2002b, 2, p. 200-206.

Meszaros, I., Morocz, J., Szlavi, J., et al. 2000. Epidemiology and clinicopathology of aortic dissection. Chest, 2000, 5, p. 1271-1278.

Milewicz, D. M., Michael, K., Fisher, N., et al. 1996. Fibrillin-1 (FBN1) mutations in patients with thoracic aortic aneurysms. Circulation, 1996, 11, p. 2708-2711.

Minatoya, K., Karck, M., Hagl, C., et al. 2002. The impact of spinal angiography on the neurological outcome after surgery on the descending thoracic and thoracoabdominal aorta. Ann Thorac Surg, 2002, 5, p. S1870-1872; discussion S1892-1878.

Mokráček, A., Pavel, P., Šetina, M., et al. 2000. Onemocnění vzestupné hrudní aorty a aortálního oblouku: naše indikace a výsledky operační léčby. Cor Vasa, 2000, 9, p. 444-448.

Mokráček, A., Peregrin, P. H., Hejnal, J., et al. 2001. Percutaneous management of descending thoracic aorta dissection in experiment using uncoated and coated stents. Cor Vasa, 2001, 3, p. 115-120.

Molinero-Herguedas, E., Labrador-Fuster, T., Rios-Lazaro, M., et al. 2008. [Aortic aneurysm in Alagille syndrome]. Rev Esp Cardiol, 2008, 6, p. 658-659.

Mulder, B. J. 2008. The distal aorta in the Marfan syndrome. Neth Heart J, 2008, 11, p. 382-386.

Munakata, M., Hirotani, T., Nakamichi, T., et al. 2004. Mycotic aneurysm of the descending aorta with hemoptysis. Ann Thorac Cardiovasc Surg, 2004, 5, p. 314-316.

Narayan, P., Alwair, H., Bryan, A. J. 2004. Surgical resection of sequential thoracic aortic aneurysms in Wiskott-Aldrich syndrome. Interact Cardiovasc Thorac Surg, 2004, 2, p. 346-348.

Nataf, P., Lansac, E. 2006. Dilation of the thoracic aorta: medical and surgical management. Heart, 2006, 9, p. 1345-1352.

Němec, P., Černý, J., Wagner, R., et al. 1998. Náhrada ascendentní aorty konduitem s chlopní a reimplantací koronárních tepen. Cor Vasa, 1998, 7, p. 326-328.

Niederle, P. 2005. Echokardiografie dospělých 1. díl. Praha: Triton, 2005. 396 p.

Nienaber, C. A., Eagle, K. A. 2003. Aortic dissection: new frontiers in diagnosis and management: Part I: from etiology to diagnostic strategies. Circulation, 2003, 5, p. 628-635.

Nienaber, C.A., Rousseau, H., Eggebrecht, H., et al. 2009. Randomized comparison of strategies for type B aortic dissection: the INvestigation of STEnt Grafts in Aortic Dissection (INSTEAD) trial. Circulation, 2009, 25, p. 2519-2528.

Nijs, A., Vandekerkhof, J., Cartuyvels, R., et al. 2002. Streptococcus pneumoniae-infected aneurysm extending from a persistent lobar pneumonia: case report and review of the literature. Eur J Clin Microbiol Infect Dis, 2002, 5, p. 389-392.

Nistri, S., Sorbo, M. D., Marin, M., et al. 1999. Aortic root dilatation in young men with normally functioning bicuspid aortic valves. Heart, 1999, 1, p. 19-22.

Nuenninghoff, D. M., Warrington, K. J., Matteson, E. L. 2003. Concomitant giant cell aortitis, thoracic aortic aneurysm, and aortic arch syndrome: occurrence in a patient and significance. Arthritis Rheum, 2003, 6, p. 858-861.

Park, C. B., Greason, K. L., Suri, R. M., et al. 2011. Should the proximal arch be routinely replaced in patients with bicuspid aortic valve disease and ascending aortic aneurysm? J Thorac Cardiovasc Surg, 2011, 3, p. 602-607.

Pasic, M., Hetzer, R. 1999. Saccular aneurysm of the aortic arch. Ann Thorac Surg, 1999, 1, p. 257.

Petasnick, J. P. 1991. Radiologic evaluation of aortic dissection. Radiology, 1991, 2, p. 297-305.

Piazza, N., De Jaegere, P., Schultz, C., et al. 2008. Anatomy of the aortic valvar complex and its implications for transcatheter implantation of the aortic valve. Circ Cardiovasc Interv, 2008, 1, p. 74-81.

Piler, P., Fila, P. 2008. Aneurysm of the thorcic aorta. Kardiol Rev Int Med, 2008, 1, p. 18-25.

Pretre, R., Von Segesser, L. K. 1997. Aortic dissection. Lancet, 1997, 9063, p. 1461-1464.

Price, W. H., Wilson, J. 1983. Dissection of the aorta in Turner's syndrome. J Med Genet, 1983, 1, p. 61-63.

Purnell, R., Williams, I., Von Oppell, U., et al. 2005. Giant aneurysms of the sinuses of Valsalva and aortic regurgitation in a patient with Noonan's syndrome. Eur J Cardiothorac Surg, 2005, 2, p. 346-348.

Radl, J., Dooren, L. H., Morell, A., et al. 1976. Immunoglobulins and transient paraproteins in sera of patients with the Wiskott-Aldrich syndrome: a follow-up study. Clin Exp Immunol, 1976, 2, p. 256-263.

Radunovic, Z., Wekre, L. L., Diep, L. M., et al. 2011. Cardiovascular abnormalities in adults with osteogenesis imperfecta. Am Heart J, 2011, 3, p. 523-529.

Raupach, J., Lojík, M., Krajina, A., et al. 2006. Atypická aneuryzmata hrudní a břišní aorty: diagnostika a léčba. Miniinvazivní metody ve vnitřním lékařství. 2006, 1, p. 39-43.

Roberts, J.R., 2014 [on line]. Takayasu Arteritis. In: Medscape [citované 12. December 2014]. < http://emedicine.medscape.com/article/332378-overview- >

Rojo-Leyva, F., Ratliff, N. B., Cosgrove, D. M., 3rd, et al. 2000. Study of 52 patients with idiopathic aortitis from a cohort of 1,204 surgical cases. Arthritis Rheum, 2000, 4, p. 901-907.

Rosman, H. S., Patel, S., Borzak, S., et al. 1998. Quality of history taking in patients with aortic dissection. Chest, 1998, 3, p. 793-795.

Sabol, F., Bily, B., Kolesár. A., et al. 2014. Hybrid repair of arch aneurysm. Cor et vasa, 56 (2014), e523-e526.

Sabol, F., Kolesár, A., Toporcer, T., et al. 2014. Surgical management of a hypoplastic distal aortic arch and coarctation of aorta in a patient with Klippel-Feil syndrome, ascending aortic aneurysm and bicuspid aortic valve. Interact Cardiovasc Thorac Surg, 2014, p. 708-710.

Sabol, F., Mistríková, L., Kolesár, A., et al. 2014. One-stage surgical approach to coarctation of the aorta and ascending aortic aneurysm. BratislMedJ, 2014, 115 (9), p. 593-596.

Sadler, T.W., et al. 2011. Langman's Medical Embryology. Philadelphia: LWW, 2011. 400 p.

Sakomura, Y., Nagashima, H., Aoka, Y., et al. 2002. Expression of peroxisome proliferator-activated receptor-gamma in vascular smooth muscle cells is upregulated in cystic medial degeneration of annuloaortic ectasia in Marfan syndrome. Circulation, 2002, 12 Suppl 1, p. I259-263.

Salvarani, C., Pipitone, N., Versari, A., et al. 2005. Positron emission tomography (PET): evaluation of chronic periaortitis. Arthritis Rheum, 2005, 2, p. 298-303.

Schäfers, H.J., Aicher, D., Riodionycheva, S., et al. 2008. Bicuspidization of the unicuspid aortic valve: a new reconstructive approach. Ann Thorac Surg, 2008, p. 2012-8.

Schmid, F. X., Bielenberg, K., Holmer, S., et al. 2004. Structural and biomolecular changes in aorta and pulmonary trunk of patients with aortic aneurysm and valve disease: implications for the Ross procedure. Eur J Cardiothorac Surg, 2004, 5, p. 748-753.

Song, J. M., Kim, H. S., Song, J. K., et al. 2003. Usefulness of the initial noninvasive imaging study to predict the adverse outcomes in the medical treatment of acute type A aortic intramural hematoma. Circulation, 2003, p. II324-328.

Soravia-Dunand, V. A., Loo, V. G., Salit, I. E. 1999. Aortitis due to Salmonella: report of 10 cases and comprehensive review of the literature. Clin Infect Dis, 1999, 4, p. 862-868.

Standring, S. 2008. Gray's Anatomy: The Anatomical Basis of Clinical Practice, Expert Consult – Online and Print, 40e. London: Churchill Livingstone, 2008. 1576 p.

Steiner, R. D. 2009. Ehlers – Danlos syndrome. Medscape, 2009.

Sueyoshi, E., Sakamoto, I., Hayashi, K. 2000. Aortic aneurysms in patients with Takayasu's arteritis: CT evaluation. AJR Am J Roentgenol, 2000, 6, p. 1727-1733.

Sullivan, J.A., 2012. [on line]. Klippel-Feil Syndrome. In: Medscape [citované 12. December 2014]. < http://emedicine.medscape.com/article/1264848-overview- >

Suresh, K., Kurian, V. M., Madhu Sankar, N., et al. 2003. Repair of tuberculous aneurysm of distal aortic arch. Asian Cardiovasc Thorac Ann, 2003, 4, p. 346-348.

Suzuki, T., Katoh, H., Watanabe, M., et al. 1996. Novel biochemical diagnostic method for aortic dissection. Results of a prospective study using an immunoassay of smooth muscle myosin heavy chain. Circulation, 1996, 6, p. 1244-1249.

Suzuki, T., Mehta, R. H., Ince, H., et al. 2003. Clinical profiles and outcomes of acute type B aortic dissection in the current era: lessons from the International Registry of Aortic Dissection (IRAD). Circulation, 2003, p. II312-317.

Svensson, L. G., Hess, K. R., Coselli, J. S., et al. 1994. Influence of segmental arteries, extent, and atriofemoral bypass on postoperative paraplegia after thoracoabdominal aortic operations. J Vasc Surg, 1994, 2, p. 255-262.

Svensson, L. G., Labib, S. B., Eisenhauer, A. C., et al. 1999. Intimal tear without hematoma: an important variant of aortic dissection that can elude current imaging techniques. Circulation, 1999, 10, p. 1331-1336.

Tang, P. C., Coady, M. A., Lovoulos, C., et al. 2005. Hyperplastic cellular remodeling of the media in ascending thoracic aortic aneurysms. Circulation, 2005, 8, p. 1098-1105.

Teixeira, A. R., Nitz, N., Guimaro, M. C., et al. 2006. Chagas disease. Postgrad Med J, 2006, 974, p. 788-798.

Tolulola, A., Adeleye, O., Pottis, J. L. et al. 2001. Thoracic aortic dissection in a patient with autosomal dominant polycystic kidney disease. J Natl Med Assoc, 2001, 93, p. 282 – 287.

Uemura, S. 1996. Influence of Aneurysm Shape on Wall Stress: Finite Element Study. Washington: University of Washington, 1996. 202 p.

Umscheid, T. W., Rouhani, G., Morlang, T., et al. 2007. Hemangiosarcoma after endovascular aortic aneurysm repair. J Endovasc Ther, 2007, 1, p. 101-105.

Varma, P. K., Neelakandhan, K. S. 2006. Syphilitic aneurysm eroding the chest wall. Asian Cardiovasc Thorac Ann, 2006, 4, p. 351.

Vaglio, A., Corradi, D., Manenti, L., et al. 2003. Evidence of autoimmunity in chronic periaortitis: a prospective study. Am J Med, 2003, 6, p. 454-462.

Van Bommel, E. F. 2002. Retroperitoneal fibrosis. Neth J Med, 2002, 6, p. 231-242.

Verbrugge, E., Ennezat, P. V., Marechaux, S., et al. 2006. Staphylococcal aortitis. Eur Heart J, 2006, 17, p. 2068.

Vincelj, J. 2002. Usefulness of transesophageal echocardiography in the diagnosis of aortic dissection and aneurysm. Cardiol, 2002, 1, p. 13-20.

Vogel, P. S., Nemer, J., Sau, P., et al. 1992. Churg-Strauss syndrome. J Am Acad Dermatol, 1992, 5 Pt 2, p. 821-824.

Vojáček, J., Tuna, M., Vanekova, S., et al. 2009.Cor et Vasa Aortic valve-sparing surgery-early and mid-term outcomes. Cor et Vasa, 2009, 51(11 – 12), p. 7.

Von Kodolitsch, Y., Csosz, S. K., Koschyk, D. H., et al. 2003. Intramural hematoma of the aorta: predictors of progression to dissection and rupture. Circulation, 2003, 8, p. 1158-1163.

Von Kodolitsch, Y., Schwartz, A. G., Nienaber, C. A. 2000. Clinical prediction of acute aortic dissection. Arch Intern Med, 2000, 19, p. 2977-2982.

Wang, Y., Barbacioru, C. C., Shiffman, D., et al. 2007. Gene expression signature in peripheral blood detects thoracic aortic aneurysm. PLoS One, 2007, 10, s. e1050.

Weiler, V., Redtenbacher, S., Bancher, C., et al. 2000. Concurrence of sarcoidosis and aortitis: case report and review of the literature. Ann Rheum Dis, 2000, 11, p. 850-853.

Vejvoda, J., Alan, D., Ošťádal, P. 2005. Disekce aorty. Interv Akut Kardiol, 2005, 4, p. 159 – 165.

Williams, J. A., Loeys, B. L., Nwakanma, L. U., et al. 2007. Early surgical experience with Loeys-Dietz: a new syndrome of aggressive thoracic aortic aneurysm disease. Ann Thorac Surg, 2007, 2, p. S757-763; discussion S785-790.

Wilton, E., Bland, M., Thompson, M., et al. 2008. Matrix metalloproteinase expression in the ascending aorta and aortic valve. Interact Cardiovasc Thorac Surg, 2008, 1, p. 37-40.

Wolff, K. A., Herold, C. J., Tempany, C. M., et al. 1991. Aortic dissection: atypical patterns seen at MR imaging. Radiology, 1991, 2, p. 489-495.

Yacoub, M. H., Gehle, P., Chandrasekaran, V., et al. 1998. Late results of a valve-preserving operation in patients with aneurysms of the ascending aorta and root. J Thorac Cardiovasc Surg, 1998, 5, p. 1080-1090.

Yamada, E., Matsumura, M., Kyo, S., et al. 1995. Usefulness of a prototype intravascular ultrasound imaging in evaluation of aortic dissection and comparison with angiographic study, transesophageal echocardiography, computed tomography, and magnetic resonance imaging. Am J Cardiol, 1995, 2, p. 161-165.

Yamada, I., Nakagawa, T., Himeno, Y., et al. 1998. Takayasu arteritis: evaluation of the thoracic aorta with CT angiography. Radiology, 1998, 1, p. 103-109.

Yankah, C. A., Weng. Y., Hetzer R., et al. 2010. Aortic Root Surgery.: The Bilogical Solution. Springer-Verlag. Heidelberg, 2010. 616 p.

Yasuda, H., Nakatani, S., Stugaard, M., et al. 2003. Failure to prevent progressive dilation of ascending aorta by aortic valve replacement in patients with bicuspid aortic valve: comparison with tricuspid aortic valve. Circulation, 2003, p. II291-294.

Zaki, S. A., Shenoy, P., Shanbag, P. 2010. Klippel Feil syndrome with isolated hypokinesia of the left ventricle: A rare association. Ann Pediatr Cardiol, 2010, 1, p. 92.

Zalts, R., Hamoud, S., Bar-Shalom, R., et al. 2005. Panaortitis: diagnosis via fluorodeoxyglucose positron emission tomography. Am J Med Sci, 2005, 5, p. 247-249.

Zehr, K. J., Mathur, A., Orszulak, T. A., et al. 2005. Surgical treatment of ascending aortic aneurysms in patients with giant cell aortitis. Ann Thorac Surg, 2005, 5, p. 1512-1517.

František Sabol, assoc. prof., MD, PhD, MPH (1967) is the Head at the Clinic of Cardiac Surgery at the East Slovak Institute of Cardiovascular Disease (VÚSCH,a. s.) and Faculty of Medicine at Pavol JozefŠafárik University (UPJŠ) in Košice. He completed his doctoral studies at the Faculty of Medicine at Pavol Jozef Šafárik University in Košice in 1991. During 1992-97, Dr. Sabol worked at the First Surgery Clinic of L. Pasteur Teaching Hospital in Košice. He has also completed study programs at a variety of cardiac surgery facilities, such as the Slovak Institute of Cardiovascular Diseases in Bratislava, IKEM Prague, Hadassah Hebrew University in Jerusalem, and at the Uniklinik in Bonn, Germany. Since 1997, Dr. Sabol has focused on cardiac surgery in Košice. In 2007, he became Head of the Department of Cardiac Surgery at the VÚSCH, a. s. and since 2009 also assumed the role of a Head Surgeon at the Clinic of Cardiac Surgery at the VÚSCH a.s. Dr. Sabol has served at the highest managerial role at VUSCH, a. s. for a number of years, and is also a vice dean at the Faculty of Medicine at Pavol Josef Šafárik University in Košice. He has passed four postgraduate specializations andMaster of Public Health (MPH) degree. In the 2015 he also successfully completed his senior lectureship in surgery in Faculty of Medicine at UPJŠ. He is also a member of the Czech Society of Cardiovascular Surgery and the Slovak Society of Cardiology. Since 2012, Dr. Sabol is the subject matter expert for the Slovak Ministry of Health for cardiac surgery. He has authored a textbook "Basic Principles of Cardiac Surgery" (UPJŠ,2015), co-authored an textbook titled "Základy všeobecnej chirurgie pre štúdium ošetrovateľstva" (Aprilla, 2007), co-authored a monographs titled "Angiogenéza a lymfangiogenéza" (Institute of Veterinary Medicine, UPJŠ, 2005) and "Základné zásady transportu kriticky chorého pacienta a pacienta s obehovou a ventilačnou poruchou v záchranárskej praxi" (Osveta, 2015). Dr. Sabol has authored and co-authored 98 published scientific papers and 105 lectures on cardiac surgery and related topics.

Adrian Kolesár, MD, PhD (1971) is the Vice head at the Clinic of Cardiac Surgery at the East Slovak Institute of Cardiovascular Disease (VÚSCH, a. s.) and Faculty of Medicine at Pavol Jozef Šafárik University (UPJŠ) in Košice. He received his medical degree from the First Faculy of Medicine at the Charles University in Prague in 1996. From 1996-2000, Dr. Kolesár worked at the cardiovascular and transplant surgery department at the Institute for Clinical and Experimental Medicine, while also working at the general surgery department of the Tomayer hospital. From 2000-07, he worked at the cardiac surgery clinic at the University hospital in Motol, while also practicing at the vascular department at the Na Homolce Hospital in Prague. In 2004, Dr. Kolesár completed a study program at the Herzzentrum Leipzig – Universitätsklinik in Leipzig. Since 2008 he has worked at the Clinic of Cardiac Surgery at the UPJŠand VÚSCH, a. s. in Košice, becoming vice head in 2010. He has completed three postgraduate specializations and is currently in his 3 rd year of pursuing a Master of Public Health (MPH) degree. Dr. Kolesár also a member of the Czech Society of Cardiovascular Surgery, Czech Society of Cardiology and the Slovak Society of Cardiology, the European Association for Cardio-Thoracic Surgery and the Heart Valve Society. Since 2012, he works as the regional subject matter expert on cardiac surgery for the Slovak Ministry of Health. Dr. Kolesár is the co-author of the monograph titled "Základné zásady transportu kriticky chorého pacienta a pacienta s obehovou a ventilačnou poruchou v záchranárskej praxi" (Osveta, 2015). In addition, he authored and/or co-authored 35 published scientific articles and more than 68 lectures on the topic of cardiac surgery.

Panagiotis Artemiou, MD, PhD. (1968) works as a doctor at the Clinic of Cardiac Surgery at the East Slovak Institute of Cardiovascular Disease (VÚSCH, a. s.) and Faculty of Medicine at Pavol Jozef Šafárik University (UPJŠ) in Košice. In 1995, he graduated with a medical degree from the Comenius University Faculty of Medicine in Bratislava. He has practiced medicine at the following institutions:

1995-96:   Nicosia General Hospital, Cyprus – department of internal medicine and general surgery;

1996-97:   Hadassah Hebrew University in Jeruzaleme – department of cardiac surgery;

1997-98:   L. Pasteur Teaching Hospital in Košice – department of cardiac surgery.

Additional Workplaces:

1999-2005: Chaim Sheba Medical Center, Tel-Aviv;

2005-07:   Interbalcan Medical Center, Thessaloniki;

2007-10:   Kyanous Stavros, Thessaloniki;

2010-11:   Euroclinic of Athens.

Since November 2013 until now, Dr. Panagiotis has worked as a cardiac surgeon at the East Slovak Institute of Cardiovascular Disease (VÚSCH a.s.) in Košice. He is a member of the Greek Society for Cardiac Surgery, Medical Association of Thessaloniki, Cypress Medical Society and the General Medical Council in Great Britain. He is an author and/or co-author of 20 scientific papers and ten lectures. He also co-authored a university textbook titled "Basic Principles of Cardiac Surgery" (UPJŠ, 2015).

Review of the Diseases of the Aorta
Book authored by Sabol F., Kolesár A. and Artemiou P.

The topic of this book is diseases of the aorta, which is a group of diseases that perhaps is not large in number; however, it is one of utmost importance not only for patients, but also for physicians, especially since their diagnostics and treatment are not simple.

The book is conceptually interesting and in many aspects unique. The first chapter provides a very detailed description of aortic embryology, histology and anatomy accompanied with numerous photographs and schematics, which provide the reader with a comprehensive picture.

In the section on diagnostic options, emphasis is placed on the significant role of computer tomography, with descriptions of additional options such as echocardiography and magnetic resonance.

Large portions of the text are devoted to detailed pathophysiological descriptions. Both from the perspective of the reasons and speed associated with aortic diametre expansion and also from the perspective of the reasons for aneurysm formation at the microscopic level. The text describes processes of destruction of the extracellular matrix and destruction of leiomyocytes, angiogenesis etc. This data will allow the reader to peek behind curtain of aneurysm formation.

The next chapter summarises etiological factors of aneurysm formation. Here, analysis of not only the most common causes are discussed, such as atherosclerosis, hypertension, and basic genetic malformations (Marfan syndrome), but also less known or even rare causes (most common due to congenital malformations). The reader is reminded of the almost unbelievable diseases in which an aneurysm should be considered as a cause. Similarly, the reader also learns which diseases to keep in mind should an aneurysm be confirmed. The effect the bicuspid aortic valve may have on aneurysm formation is described as well.

A very interesting chapter is the one on inflammatory infectious and non-infectious causes. Important information for a surgeon is the fact that an inflammatory process can cause suture dehiscence from either a vascular prosthesis or aortic valve. Therefore, with inflammatory etiology, suture dehiscence should be considered and such surgical procedures should be used that would prevent a leak or pseudoaneurysm formation.

The most substantial chapter from a surgeon's perspective is the one on treatment options, described in a comprehensive manner. An entire chapter is dedicated to the acute aortic syndrome caused by Type A aortic dissection, transection and necessity of an emergency surgical or endovascular intervention. The reference list to which many references in the text of the book are made is extensive and includes well-known and important publications relevant to the book's topic.

The book is written by Sabol et al. "Diseases of the Aorta" describes a wide scale of thoracic aorta diseases. Thanks to the efforts of the authors to penetrate the core essence of the diseases, the book is in many aspects an exceptional work. Reading it can be recommended not only to cardiac surgeons and cardiologists, but also to internists and general surgeons. Some chapters can be recommended even to doctors of other specialties, who may find in this book a plethora of new and interesting information and, therefore, it will increase their knowledge in the area of diseases of the thoracic aorta.

Assoc. Prof. Petr Nemec, MD, CSc, MBA, FETCS

Review of the Diseases of the Aorta
Book authored by Sabol F., Kolesár A. and Artemiou P.

The book by authors Sabol, F., Kolesár, A., and Artemiou, P., comprehensively summarises current knowledge on albeit uncommon, but serious aortic diseases. It is a publication with a cross-specialty reach. Until now, diseases of the aorta were part of texts from the area of internal medicine, angiology, imaging methods, vascular surgery, and cardiac surgery. The importance and need for such a publication is demonstrated in day-to-day practice. Due to the improvements in diagnostic methods and subsequent earlier diagnosis, patients with some of these aortic diseases are no longer a rarity and it is expected that with the increase in survival rates, we will be encountering them more often.

The authors succeeded in creating a work that summarises a vast amount of knowledge into a unified, concise, and clear form. The sequence of the chapters is logical, starting with a historical overview. Anatomical notes are written in a way that takes into consideration the most prevalent occurrence of diseases and treatment options. Chapters on embryology, pathophysiology, and diagnostic tools are well documented pictorially and provide the necessary information for understanding the origin and diagnostic options of each individual pathological state and related therapies.

Very useful is the chapter on aneurysm etiology. It presents an overview of all etiological groups, allowing the reader to become versed in the topic, while pointing out the less known aneurysm causes. The sub-chapter on aortic aneurysm treatment provides a clear and understandable summary of the indication criteria and treatment options. A separate chapter is dedicated to acute aortic states – aortic dissection and transection. The biggest merit of this publication is its rich and descriptive pictorial documentation.

In our hands we have a comprehensive book, which to a large degree fills a gap in the market, one that addresses the needs of the medical community of all specialists, but also of general practitioners, who come across patients with aortic diseases in the course of their practice. For this, the authors deserve our acknowledgement and appreciation.

Assoc. Prof. Vilem Rohn, MD, CSc